Echeverias

Echeverias

A guide to cultivation and identification of the popular American succulents

by

L. CARRUTHERS and R. GINNS

ARCO PUBLISHING COMPANY, INC
New York

Published by Arco Publishing Company, Inc
219 Park Avenue South, New York, N.Y. 10003

Library of Congress Catalog Card
Number 73–76585

ISBN 0–668–02966–8

Printed in Great Britain

CONTENTS

LIST OF COLOUR PLATES

35. Silveron Red
36. *Echeveria affinis*
37. Gypsy
38. *Echeveria harmsii*
39. Echeveria x Mary Butterfield
40. *Echeveria x purpurea*
41. *Echeveria runyonii* Inflorescence
42. *Echeveria nodulosa*
43. *Echeveria sedoides*
44. *Echeveria multicaulis*
45. *Echevaria atropurpurea*
46. Echevaria x Bittersweet
47. Echeveria x Gilva cv. 'Blue Surprise'
48. A mixed collection of Echeveria

ACKNOWLEDGEMENTS

The authors wish to acknowledge the help given them in the preparation of this book. The checking of most of the data by Mr. J. C. van Keppel of Holland, who has an exceptional library of information on the genus. Mr. C. Williams of Preston who also advised on nomenclatural problems. Mr. J. Napton of America for his research in the History of the Echeveria as published in the American Society Journal from which our notes on the History is based. Mr. D. Wright of California, U.S.A., for the supply of photographs of his specimen hybrid introductions and Mr. W. Sandham of Blackburn for his patient photographic work for all the remaining photographs in this book.

FOREWORD

Echeveria come in a variety of shapes and sizes, from dwarf branched sub-shrubs to plants with huge cabbage-like symmetrical rosettes with hairy or waxy leaves in all colours of the spectrum, from nearly white to dark purple. Specimen plants will flower all the year round, some carrying white, yellow, pink, red or bicolour bell shaped flowers on elegant racemes, spike or cymes. These are Echeverias in the broadest sense.

When in 1828, the great botanist De Candolle established this genus only three species were known to him. Nowadays there are over one hundred described species, coming from Texas, Mexico, Central and South America. In the height of their popularity around 1870 various commercial growers raised many hybrids, some of which can still be found in collections today more than one hundred years later.

The popularity of Echeverias over the last few years has again increased and this book written by two keen growers of the genus, Les Carruthers and Ron Ginns will be found to be a trustworthy guide to all who are interested in these succulents, dealing with cultivation and other problems. It will also be found to be a good introduction on the new and old varieties to be found in general cultivation to-day. A book on these plants has been long overdue and I trust it will enlarge the popularity of the genus Echeveria still further.

J. C. van Keppel

Holland

INTRODUCTION

Fifteen years ago when we first became interested in the genus, few Echeverias were known in English collections. For that matter the same could be said about most succulents. Lack of fuel for greenhouses during the war had led to the loss of most succulents in the country and lack of foreign exchange in the post-war years prevented the importation of fresh material in quantity. Importers concentrated on the most popular varieties and few Echeverias came within this category.

Most collectors of succulents looked on Echeverias with rather a jaundiced eye as they were considered to be beginners' plants, their propagation and cultivation offering little challenge. Whilst this may be true of some species, e.g. *glauca, elegans, microcalyx* etc., the same cannot be said of many of the newer species.

In the 1950s the search for fresh Echeverias was like a game of "hunt the thimble". What could not be obtained from nurseries could sometimes be obtained from private collections and there were also overseas contacts to be made. Perhaps as much pleasure could be obtained from the search for new varieties as in actually growing them. Having obtained about 50 varieties one was fortunate in being able to add two or three new ones each year.

The 1960s saw a big change in the succulent scene and, with a big enough bank balance, almost any species of succulent could be obtained. Even so, new Echeverias remained elusive, mainly because of lack of demand. However, considerable progress has been made as the following pages, showing plants in the authors' collections, will show, compared with the Appendix showing named species not yet in general cultivation in England.

Whilst many previously described species still need collecting, in the late 1950s Walther in the States described 20 new species most of which we have succeeded in adding to our collections. He was engaged in writing a monograph on the genus when he was struck down by a heart attack in July, 1959. We are still awaiting the publication of the monograph. Meanwhile his work on new species has been carried on by Moran who has described a further 7 species.

In addition to this influx of new species American growers have been engaged in producing a large range of very colourful hybrids, made available to us by Mr. D. Wright of California. Mr. J. C. van Keppel in Holland has done much work investigating the parentage of the older hybrids. There is thus ample new material constantly coming forward to keep lovers of the genus occupied.

This book is not intended as a botanical monograph and is not intended to compete with Walther's book. It is intended for non-botanists who enjoy the remarkable variety of colour and form displayed by the genus. Thus there are no botanical descriptions but brief, and, we hope, readable notes have been compiled to enable collectors to check on the names of their plants, since far too much confusion still exists in the nomenclature of Echeveria species.

A HORTICULTURAL HISTORY

The horticultural history of the genus Echeveria has more than just a casual beginning, had it not been for the astonishing foresight of Augustin Pyramus De Candolle (1778–1841) all traces of the works contained in the *Flora Mexicana* and the reasons for naming the genus would have vanished.

Our story unfolds with a Royal Patent issued in 1788 by Charles III of Spain establishing a botanical expedition to Mexico under the direction of Martin Sesse, a trained scientist and botanist, but before he could sail for Mexico Charles III died and the support of Sesse could have expected in the way of finance etc., died with him. Not only was this a bad start to the expedition, worse was to follow.

Sesse embarked for Mexico in 1789 and established himself in Mexico City where he assembled a dedicated staff which included Jose Mocino with Atanasio Echeverria acting as technical illustrator to create a monumental "Flora of Mexico". Literally thousands of plants were collected, drawn and tentatively identified under the then new Linnaean system, hundreds of living specimens were collected in numerous field trips and sent to botanical gardens in Mexico City and Spain. During the 15 years of collecting, there was a constant struggle for funds, not only to continue, but to actually survive, and at times the group had no money for food or clothing.

Charles III's successor, Charles IV had no interest in botany or horticulture, and could not care less what happened to the dedicated group. When one reads the account of their work in the *Chronica Botanica*, it is remarkable that the little group survived the ordeal, working year after year under the extreme

13

hardship of disease, dysentery, hunger and chronic shortage of funds.

In 1803 Sesse returned to Spain with Mocino and Echeverria who was to complete his unfinished drawings, and they were confident that they would be famous men in Europe. Both the magnitude of their work and the rising interest in the botanical field after the creation of major botanical gardens through all the countries of Europe seemed to indicate their enthusiasm was warranted.

They were given no hearing at the Spanish Court, Charles IV cared nothing for the work of the expedition or for the man who carried out the work requested by his predecessor. Sesse returned to his small estates taking Mocino with him and into his family. Echeverria with his outstanding skill was hired by a Spanish artist.

On Sesse's death in 1809, Mocino obtained employment at the Museum of Natural History in Madrid, at the same time becoming the sole curator of all the material containing Flora Mexicana. While there, he made his first contact with Augustin Pyramus De Candolle. Wealthy, brilliant and from a socially prominent Swiss family, he was Professor of Botany at Montpellier in France from 1808 to 1816 making many botanical contributions to the field of Physiology, Morphology and Taxonomy.

Meanwhile, the shadow of Napoleon fell on the Pyrenees, the French army overrunning Spain. Mocino was torn between a desire to stay in Madrid at his post, or flee before the French soldiers, here one finds contradictory reports, but it seems Mocino loaded the precious Flora Mexicana material on an ox cart and fled before the French army to De Candolle at Montpellier. After 1816 De Candolle returned to Geneva, taking Mocino with him and the precious material. In 1820 Mocino returned to Madrid and his job at the Museum, leaving all his plants and the drawings with De Candolle. Later he wrote De Candolle asking for all the material to be returned to him.

What occurs next ties the past with the present and the story came to us from Alphonse De Candolle, son of Augustin and also a botanist. Because De Candolle both feared for the future preservation of what he considered priceless botanical material, and because he had not completed his study of it, he hired 120 draughtsmen to work for 10 days making precise tracings of the Echeverria drawings, these being executed on 12in. × 9in. sheets of the finest tissue paper available and traced with needle-sharp hard lead pencils.

De Candolle's forethought in this regard was indeed superb, as an honourable man, he returned all the originals to Mocino in Madrid. At this time little is known of Mocino, sufficient to say all the herbarium specimens, records and the Echeverria drawings, some 2,400 became lost.

De Candolle first named the genus Echeveria in an address on the Crassulaceae given before the Society of Natural History in Geneva, 15th February, 1827. In discussing his choice of a name for the genus, he said: "I have given to this Mexican genus the name of Echeveria in honour of Echeverria, gifted botanical draughtsman and creator of the most beautiful drawings of the Flora Mexicana begun under the direction of Messrs. Sesse, Mocino and Cervantes."

One set of the De Candolle tracings was discovered by Mr. J. Napton and Professor R. Harlan at the University of California in 1967. Mr. Napton states in the *American Cactus and Succulent Journal*: "When we first saw the two great folios which contained these tracings we were almost afraid to open them. Only the three prefactory leaves by Alphonse De Candolle are printed dated 1874 approximately 50 years after his father had the tracings made. The two volumes weigh nearly 30lb. each, containing heavy stock pages on which are pasted the exquisitely executed tracings of Echeverria's drawings for the Flora Mexicana. The tracings are exactly as Echeverria left the drawings, many with details unfinished."

Since the early 1800's many notable men, botanists, enthusiastic plant growers and amateurs, have made valuable contributions to our knowledge of Echeveria, and even today, men such as Reid Moran of the U.S.A. and Joop van Keppel of Holland continue the dedicated work of their contemporaries listed below in describing new species as they become available and investigating old hybrids of unknown parentage. Arranged

15

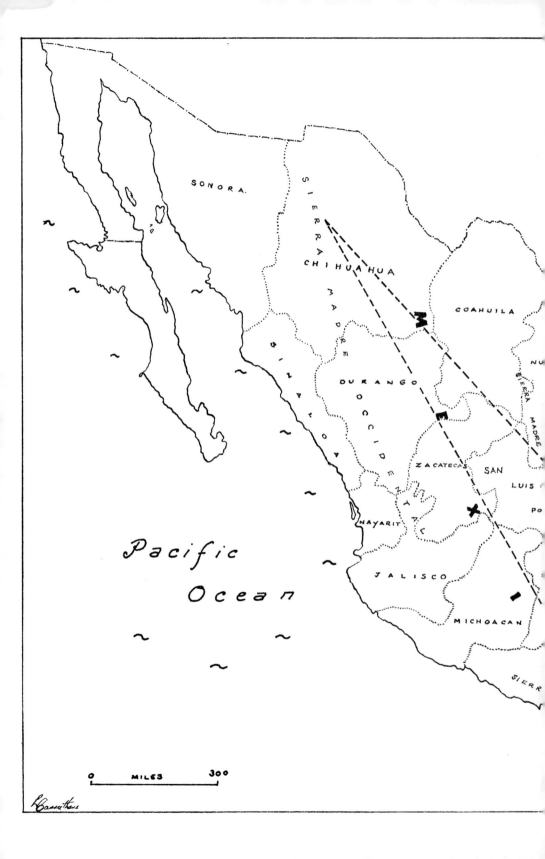

SONORA.

CHIHUAHUA

COAHUILA

SIERRA MADRE OCCIDENTE

DURANGO

SINALOA

ZACATECAS

SAN LUIS PO

SIERRA MADRE

NAYARIT

JALISCO

MICHOACAN

SIERR

Pacific

Ocean

0   MILES   300

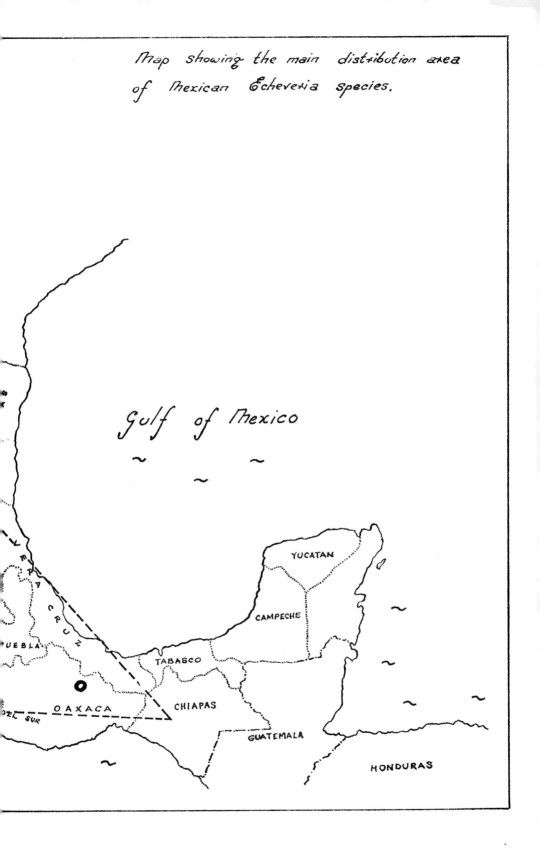

Map showing the main distribution area of Mexican Echeveria species.

then in chronological order are only some of the men who have named species in the genus Echeveria:

De Candolle, Augustin Pyramus (1778–1841) Geneva, Switzerland

Established the genus on the 15th February, 1827 in an address to the Society of Natural History in Geneva. Naming E. coccinea, (type species) *E. gibbiflora and E. teretifolia.* E. teretifolia is imperfectly known except for an incomplete drawing and if the plant was a rosette form, De Candolle never mentioned it in his description. To this day it has remained among the imperfectly known plants and is not in cultivation.

Lindley, John (1799–1865) English

One of our most distinguished botanists and botanical authors who wrote *Digitalium Monographia,* 1821, and *An Introduction to the Natural System of Botany,* 1830. He described five Echeveria: *E. acutifolia* (1842 Edwards Botanical Register); *E. nuda* (1856 Gardeners Chronical); *E. quitensis* (1852 Journal of the Royal Horticultural Society); *E. rosea* (1842 Botanical Register 22); *E. sheeri* (1845 Botanical Register t. 27).

Baker, John Gilbert (1834–1920) English

In 1869 Baker wrote the first revision of Echeveria in which he described 34 species, illustrating 16. (The American species of Cotyledon (Echeveria DC) Refugium Botanicum 1: plates 56–71.) He had a distinguished career as Keeper of the Herbarium at the Royal Gardens at Kew.

Purpus, Joseph Anton (1860–1932) German

A former superintendent of the Botanical Gardens in Darmstadt, Germany, he described six Echeveria, most of which are common today even in general collections except for *E. subalpina,* a plant which is imperfectly known in England. *E. derenbergii, E. gigantea, E. leucotricha, E. pilosa, E. setosa, E. subalpina.*

Rose, Joseph Nelson (1862–1928) American

Assistant curator of the Division of plants, U.S. National Museum at the Smithsonia Institute, a co-author with Britton in producing the four volume work *The Cactaceae,* 1919–23.

He specialised in the crassulaceae and North American Cactaceae, naming altogether almost forty Echeveria.

Walther, Eric (1892–1959) Born Dresden, Germany

The Director of the Strybing Arboretum and Botanical Garden in the Golden Gate Park, San Francisco, California, U.S.A. until he retired in 1957. Walther specialised for over 24 years in the genus Echeveria. On his retirement in 1957 he became a Research Associate of the California Academy of Sciences preparing his still unpublished monograph of the genus, when he died suddenly of a heart attack on 1st July, 1959. His work has been a major contribution to our knowledge of the genus.

HABITAT

Most of the species of Echeveria come from the southern and eastern States of Mexico. Puebla, Vera Cruz, San Luis Potosi and Oaxaca especially. Some range south into Chiapas and further still into South America. From Oaxaca the distribution spreads north in a narrowing triangle across the high plateau of the Mesa Central and the edge of the Sierra Madre Occidental as far north as Chihuahua, giving a very wide geographical distribution. Only one species of Echeveria can be found as far north as Texas, U.S.A., this is *E. strictiflora*. The reason why the plants centre on the region of Oaxaca and Puebla and in the main spread north instead of south and east rather than west in Mexico is apparent from the physical structure and rainfall of the area.

In the normal way Mexico would be very wet from the one rain-bearing trade wind that crosses it from the Gulf of Mexico, providing a regular, almost all the year round, supply of rain from these winds, but on leaving the east coast the trade wind is forced to rise by the natural mountain barriers of the Sierra Madre Oriental and Sierra Madre del Sur ranges causing a drop in wind temperature of 1°C. per 200m., this cooling effect on the wind gives rise to rapid condensation which falls as rain. As can be expected, this causes tropical downpours and flash floods which cut deep incised valleys and gullies into the mountain landscape facing the coast making the eastern seaboard hot and wet. Spent of excessive moisture the winds create a gentler precipitous rain shadow at the high altitudes at which the Echeverias grow, some 2,500m. and over, the cooler wind and reduced rainfall making the climate colder than the latitude would suggest. Under these conditions our plants can be found clinging to vertical cliff faces, and growing in association with Sedums, Pachyphytums and other genera, on rocky hillsides among bush and pine forests in varying degrees of exposure and shade.

Quite a large number have been described from Central and South America, in Venezuela, Columbia, Equador, Peru, Bolivia and, just across the border, in Argentina.

Owing to travel difficulties in South America few of the known species from there have been introduced but recent collecting expeditions to those parts are starting to correct this. It is unfortunate that most of the cactus collectors, such as Ritter and Buining, have neglected the other succulents but Rausch and van Vliett collected several in Bolivia. Mr. Maurice Mason has collected in Equador and Mr. J. C. Wetton of Bogota, Columbia, has sent collected plants from that region to the authors.

Other species have been collected by American collectors, but before distribution, are being studied in the States. From this it will be seen that Echeverias are not of the desert areas, but of the high mountains of the Americas, growing in reasonably moist and cool areas.

NAMING AND THE INFLORESCENCE

Most of the species in our collections can be named by a study of their habit of growth and the shapes and colours of the leaves. In a few cases it is necessary to make use of the character of the inflorescence.

The inflorescence of Echeverias falls into two main groups, a raceme or spike and one or more cincinni. In addition there are intermediate forms, i.e. a raceme above with a short cincinni below. Many hybrids have inflorescences of this type which may serve as an indication that certain naturally occurring plants are natural hybrids.

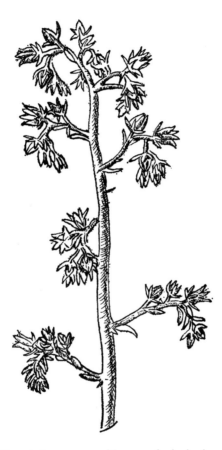

Echeveria gibbiflora inflorescence with several cincinni, usually attached singly along the main stem in a sort of raceme ($\frac{1}{2}$ size).

A Cincinnus looks like a one-sided raceme with flowers and buds in two close parallel rows, the axis of the cincinnus at first more or less zigzag with a flower at each zig and each zag. The cincinnus is curled over, and gradually straightens as successive flowers open usually starting with the lowest.

A Raceme has the flowers arranged spirally along the main axis, each on its pedicel (short stalk) in the axil of a bract which is attached on all sides of the axis and usually point in all directions. Almost always the raceme is unbranched, sometimes the flowers may turn downwards although attached on all sides of the axis giving the appearance of a cincinnus, but this is due either because the floral stem has fallen over or by unequal lighting.

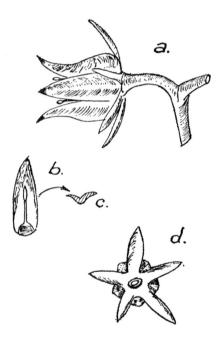

Echeveria gibbiflora var. metallica
a Flower natural size. *b* Petal interior view. *c* Cross section through petal. *d* Base view of flower showing calyx.

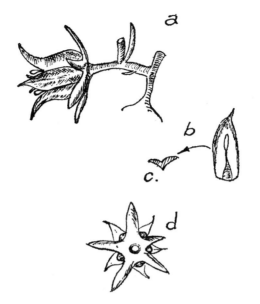

Echeveria gibbiflora var. carunculata
a Flower natural size. *b* Petal interior view, with pollen anther. *c* Cross
section through petal. *d* Base view showing calyx.

COMPOST AND CULTIVATION

We would recommend a John Innes No. 2 compost as a base for growing Echeverias, this may be modified by adding a little sharp horticultural sand and bulk in the way of leaf mould or peat if desired. The exact amount of each cannot be given as conditions vary from one part of the country to the other, also, although the compost is manufactured to the formulae evolved by the John Innes Institute and numbered 1, 2 and 3 according to the nutrient value, the basic ingredient is a good well-rotted loam and since this must vary according to the district in which it is raised, so the quality of the final product varies. It has, however, two important advantages in that it is usually well drained, by the addition of grit which is incorporated during manufacture and that the whole compost is sterilised. Soilless compost is not recommended, as Echeverias will be found to grow out of character, growing rapidly at first, with large leaves and general soft or "lush" growth with a resultant loss of colour which is the plants chief feature.

Correct watering is even more important than the right compost for success with Echeverias. It is the counsel of perfection to stand the pots in water at suitable intervals, leaving them until the water reaches the surface of the soil by capillary action. This takes far too long with a large collection of succulents which is perforce watered from above with a hose or watering can with a rose, but with Echeverias an exception is made and they are watered from *below* about once a week in summer. There are several ways of achieving this, most plants these days are potted into standard size plastic pots, for which manufacturers also provide a saucer for a little extra. It is then a simple matter to fill each individual saucer with water once a week and plants can then be moved about quite freely in the greenhouse or window-sill. For those with a greenhouse, the staging can also be adapted to carry a series of deep zinc trays with a hole drilled in one corner and with a drainage pipe blocked with a cork. The trays can then be filled with water and when the pots are soaked the corks are removed to allow excess water to drain away. These are only two methods suggested, use also could be made with polythene sheeting in lieu of trays, but this is less satisfactory.

The main point of this is that watering from above should be avoided if possible as many Echeverias are covered with a waxy bloom which causes water to collect in globules in the rosettes. This may lead to rotting and several varieties are very susceptible to this. Hard water, on evaporation, leaves a deposit of salts on the foliage which quite spoils their appearance.

It is not usual to rest Echeverias in winter like most cacti and other succulents as this causes considerable wilting of the foliage. Moreover, many species flower during winter and require water for best results. As they are relatively hardy there is no need for them to be dormant in order to resist the low temperatures. So our plants receive a smaller amount once a fortnight throughout the winter. This treatment is not, however, advisable if plants are kept at temperatures close to freezing. The combination of prolonged damp and cold causes rotting of the lower leaves and possibly complete disintegration of the rosette. If a properly heated house is not available plants must be kept dry.

As the majority of species come from the highlands of Mexico a high winter temperature is not necessary for their survival. The 5°C. (40°F.) recommended for most succulents is sufficient and many will survive some frost if quite dry.

The finest colours are to be found during February and March prior to renewed spring growth, the intensification on coloration being due to the crowding together of the red and blue pigments —anthocyanins—in the leaves. The appearance of some plants in this genus is considerably affected by growing conditions, light and shade all playing a part.

Opinions differ as to shading in summer. Providing the house is well ventilated shading is not considered necessary but, if it is not adequate enough to offset a rapid rise in temperature that can occur from March onwards, a light green shading obtainable from any good horticultural suppliers will prove advantageous in preventing leaf scorch.

The appearance of aerial roots on some species is not cause for alarm, it might at first be thought that the plant is suffering from root troubles or is pot bound but this is quite a natural occurrence with true epiphytes such as *E. rosea*.

THE GREENHOUSE

Although as we have said previously, Echeverias may be grown anywhere from a window ledge to planting outside in the rockery during the summer, for near perfect environmental growing conditions the following type of greenhouse is considered the best for them. We will not attempt to describe the construction of a greenhouse, as there are many different manufacturers producing them, at prices which make them a better proposition.

Without a doubt the best type of house for Echeveria cultivation as well as for other succulents is the "Span Type". This is a house with an equal span with the ridge in the centre and the eaves or gutter line being the same height from the ground. It receives the maximum distribution of light and enables the plants to receive full benefit if the house is positioned with the ridge or long roof facing south. In this type of house the plants are not likely to be drawn towards the lightest side. Amateur growers are well served these days by many types of manufactured span houses in all types of modern materials, Aluminium, Red Cedar wood, Rigid Plastic, etc., as well as in conventional straight grain Oak and Pine. The modern house is a vast improvement on its older counterpart. As Echeverias demand the best light possible, a modern Dutch light greenhouse with its wide spaced glazing bars in red cedar wood is recommended or if you have a deep pocket a lightweight aluminium house with its slim glazing bars is almost perfection. Besides giving the maximum light the span house also affords the maximum space, no matter how much natural light we try to provide it should be appreciated by the reader that we can only go part way and provide a small percentage of light that plants in their natural habitat of Mexico and South America would receive, which says a great deal for their adaptability to our more Northern Latitude.

Elsewhere, we have said, that the use of a light green shading in summer can be added with advantage to the outside of the glass to prevent leaf scorch when one is for instance at work all day, leaving the ventilators closed. Neither author in fact uses it, preferring instead to use the ventilators to maximum effect to keep the temperature down and when necessary leaving the door open in summer. All ventilators should be open early in the morning in anticipation of the temperature rising and not when it has already risen. This practice we employ from early spring to late autumn except when there is a possibility of frost. There is never any need to panic about high temperatures providing that ventilation is adequate, but if the high temperature is produced by sun heat only, a rise of 20°F does no harm.

Humidity in the greenhouse

Echeverias do not like conditions where there is high humidity, even if the temperature is high. This sort of atmosphere is only suitable to growing tropical jungle plants and not plants from high altitudes such as Echeverias. To help in keeping the humidity at reasonable levels especially during the cold damp winter months, it is essential to provide a full concrete floor, not just a concrete path with a side border of soil under the staging that you see in so many greenhouses. This helps considerably in reducing moisture laden air rising around the plants at a time when they are not as active as during the spring and summer.

Cleanliness in the greenhouse

It seems hardly necessary to emphasise the importance of cleanliness in the greenhouse, dead leaves and flowers stems should be removed and burnt and not just thrown down. The use of plastic pots these days obviates the tedious work entailed in scrubbing and sterilising that had to be done not many years ago with clay pots. Plastics should be sponged down in soapy water after use before stacking away.

The inside of the house should be washed down at least once a year using a mild disinfectant, and a suitable solution can be made up of Carbolic Soap to which six fluid ounces of Formaldehyde has been added. This can then be mixed with two gallons of water. Cleaning down is best done during the early summer when all the plants can be removed outside. Bench shingle or gravel if used on the staging should be washed every year at the same time as the house is washed down. This is best achieved by placing the gravel in a small mesh sieve and hosing with clean water before replacing on the bench. The number of pests that a small greenhouse can harbour during the year can be astonishing, but many, thank goodness do not appear to be interested in Echeverias.

Staging in the greenhouse

The side staging should be from 75cm. to 90cm. in height while a central staging if the greenhouse is large enough may either be of the same height or tiered. It is better to have the top removable for cleaning purposes. A permanent slatted top is sometimes used but plants placed on this type of staging should have saucers for watering, otherwise the greatly increased circulation of air tends to dry the plants out quickly in hot weather. We find that this type of staging is best covered with 3/16 or $\frac{1}{4}$in. thick asbestos sheet. It has the advantage of being rot proof and is quickly removable when cleaning the house down. A thin covering of shingle allows the plants in their pots to be plunged which keeps the pots moist over a longer period, and saves on the expense of buying individual saucers, other methods of watering are discussed elsewhere, but these points are purely personal taste as we find no difference in growth using saucers or by plunging, having tried both methods.

PESTS

There are few pests which attack Echeverias. Mealy bug is the most persistent which is often found at the base of the rosettes. The insects shelter between the base of the leaves where they are not immediately visible. They are best dealt with by using a thin pencil brush dipped in methylated spirit, the bristles of which can be inserted between the leaves. The insects are usually killed in coming in contact with the spirit which removes the white waxy coat which protects them.

A systemic insecticide can also be used with advantage, as this, if added to the water in the trays or individual plant saucers is taken up into the plant by the root system making them poisonous to Mealy bug and other injurious pests. Spraying overhead in the normal way with most plants must be avoided when dealing with Echeverias as this damages the waxy coating on the leaves of many species.

PROPAGATION

Part of the pleasure derived from a collection is in the propagation of them and the authors always endeavour to have a spare plant in case of losses, which in some instances is unavoidable and a plant lost through one cause or another is sometimes not easily replaceable.

Some collectors like to experiment with methods of increasing their stock of plants, and only a few are unsuccessful and regard the whole business as a form of black magic, but the great majority find it so easy when growing Echeverias that lack of space soon becomes a major embarrassment.

There is no doubt that the easiest, and to many collectors, the most satisfactory way, of producing new plants is by taking leaf cuttings from a healthy parent plant. By this method it is possible to produce a reasonable size plant in just over 12 months. This vegetative method has the added advantage of leaving the parent plant relatively undamaged providing the reader is not over enthusiastic in removing too many leaves.

There is no mystic about producing plants from leaf cuttings. A careful examination of a rosette will show that each leaf tapers at the base to the point where it joins the stem and it can be removed undamaged by a sideways pull. Always choose a mature leaf that shows no sign of dying back from the leaf tips, it should also be plump with no sign of dehydration. The majority of species can be propagated in this manner, but the reader should refer to the individual description notes where propagation details have been included where known.

Once leaves have been removed, they should be laid on top of a prepared John Innes compost either in pots or trays. Trays are considered more useful, as more cuttings can be accommodated, and these are then placed in half shade. A position under the greenhouse staging is ideal, and preferably raised a few inches above the ground level as slugs and snails are partial to a meal of tender leaf cuttings.

Until adventurous roots can be seen, appearing at the point on the leaf where it previously joined the stem, it is best to refrain from watering, as prior to this stage the leaves are liable to rot, especially if they have been inserted in the soil and not laid on top. Once roots have appeared, the soil should be kept moist and when the new plantlet has appeared the whole tray can be brought into the full light. This may take anything between two to six months from removing the leaves, the most popular time for this is March onwards.

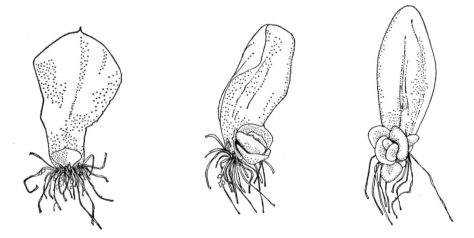

Young leaf cuttings at the safe watering stage

Offsets. Many species and hybrids produce offsets, usually from beneath the main rosette on stolons or appear between the leaves of the rosette. These, when removed by cutting or by a sideways pull, may be potted up and will quickly root. Watering should be withheld for a week to ten days to allow the cut to callus over.

Beheading. Tall species such as the *E. gibbiflora* group which eventually become ungainly, can have the rosette cut off, dried for a few days and treated as a cutting. The remaining stump should be retained and kept well watered, and this will then send out side shoots which should be pulled off and used as cuttings as soon as large enough.

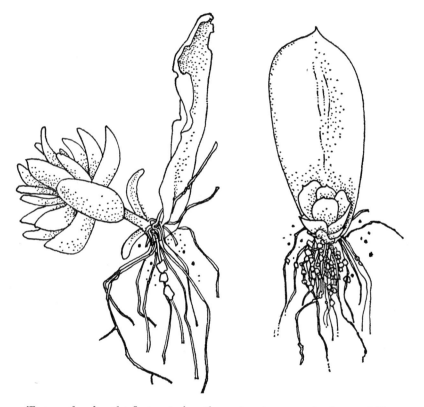

Two weeks after the first watering, the root system now develops quickly

We have not found the use of a rooting hormone powder a significant aid in the propagation of cuttings from Echeveria species or hybrids but at the same time we have not found it to be detrimental either.

31

CRISTATE ECHEVERIAS

A few cristate forms of both species and hybrids exist and although not as vigorous in growth as normal forms, they quickly make handsome specimens and unlike cristate cacti which of necessity are grafted on a more vigorous growing stock, cristate Echeveria may be grown on their own roots. At the moment they have only a novelty value as no one has attempted to collect them together to cultivate and propagate them commercially except perhaps for *E. agavoides*, the cristate form of which is well known only because nurserymen find that it is easier to propagate a large quantity of normal plants of *E. agavoides* by using the leaves from the cristate form in preference to using the leaves from the normal rosette growing plant from which leaves are difficult to remove. This propagation method leads to all sorts of trouble later on, particularly for the collector who is not aware of this as he is likely to find his normal plant reverting to the parent cristate form.

In cultivation, cristates present no special problems other than the removal of a normal shoot which may occasionally appear. This should be removed as soon as large enough to handle without damaging the crest as there is a danger of the whole plant reverting to normal if it is left on.

The following is a list of cristate forms known to us or are in our own collections:

Echeveria albicans
Echeveria agavoides
Echeveria elegans
Echeveria x 'Gilva'
Echeveria glauca
Echeveria glauca var pumila
Echeveria halbingerii
Echeveria imbricata

Echeveria gibbiflora var metallica
Echeveria x 'Mexicensis'
Echeveria multicaulis
Echeveria x 'Mutabilis'
Echeveria secunda
Echeveria setosa

1 *Echeveria pulvinata*

2 'Weingarteriana'

3 'Curly Locks'

4 *Echeveria pulvinata* cv. 'Ruby'

5 'Party Dress'

6 'Meridian'

7 'Chantilly'

8 'Edna Spencer'

9 'Cameo'

10 'H. Butterfield'

11 L. Carruthers with collection on which notes are based

12 'Mahogany Rose'

13 'Mexecensis'

14 *Echeveria rosea*

15 *Echeveria pulidonis*

16 'Fallax'

17 *Echeveria purpusorum*

18 *Echeveria multicaulis cristate*

19 'Victor Reiter'

20 'Kircheriana'

21 *E. shaviana* cv. 'Pink Frills'

22 'Haageana'

23 *E. shaviana* cv. 'Pink Frills'

24 'Mexecensis' *cristate*

25 *Echeveria johnsonii*

26 'Set-Oliver'

27 'Berkeley'

28 'Metallica'

29 'Paul Bunyan'

30 'Ballerina'

31 'Derosa' *variegata*

32 *Echeveria macdougallii*

VARIETIES

Echeveria acutifolia   Lindley
        Cotyledon acutifolia   Baker
        Echeveria holwayi   Rose

Although this plant was first described by John Lindley as long ago as 1842, it vanished from cultivation until authenticated material was distributed recently by the I.S.I.

The present plant known under this name by many collectors forms tall stems and carries a loose rosette of spatulate bronze-green leaves up to 20cm. long and 10cm. wide and is now considered to be *E. metallica* Hort of the Dutch trade and is in all probability a gibbiflora hybrid (not to be confused with *E. gibbiflora* var. metallic. Baker.).

The original description calls for a plant which carries green leaves richly touched with scarlet. Flowers are disposed in a short erect cylindrical panicle and are a rich scarlet tinged with yellow.

It originates from the state of Oaxaca, Mexico.

Propogation: By stem or leaf cuttings.

Echeveria affinis   Walther

When first introduced by the I.S.I. in 1959 it quickly became a much sought after species due to its unusual brownish black colour, and quickly became known as the Black Echeveria.

Grown in full sun and kept on the dry side, the dense rosette of thick pointed leaves become a deep brownish black, but if given shade or too much water these quickly become a dark green.

The best plants are grown from leaf cuttings, which will produce clumps of saleable size plants in two years.

The simple floral stem usually bears three to eight branches, each of which is a cincinnus terminating in a single intense red flower.

33

Its locality is near Durango, Mexico under bushes and trees.
Propogation: By leaf cuttings.

Echeveria agavoides   Lemaire
        Cotyledon agavoides Baker
         Urbinia agavoides Rose
      Echeveria yuccoides Morr

A popular easy growing species which forms large stemless
rosettes up to 20cm. across of thick pointed leaves of light apple
green tipped brown. Usually grown as a solitary specimen, sometimes forming clumps when old by offsets at the base, the leaves
are devoid of any bloom or wax coating.

The tall flower spike has reddish flowers, yellow at the apex.
Its locality is San Luis Potosi, Mexico.

Propagation: Due to the difficulty of removing the leaves, it
is best to grow new plants from leaf cuttings taken from the
cristate form.

Echeveria agavoides var. corderoyi (Baker)   Von Poellnitz

This plant was made more generally available by the I.S.I. in
1960. I.S.I. No. 322.

It is a very attractive plant with a rosette of thick pointed
leaves, a slightly darker green than the type. It is noted for its
heavy dark red leaf margins, and usually singular it does offset
with age.

Echeveria agavoides. var. cristata   Hort

This is a most attractive crest, forming large, single cocks-
combs. If the ends of the crest are allowed to grow over to touch
the soil, the shape contorts and twists until it folds into itself to
gradually form a cushion. Leaves are small, pointed and red
tipped, and it seldom offsets so that there is no tendency to revert
to type as happens with other cristate Echeverias. Offsets which
do appear should be removed to preserve the shape.

Propagation: Cuttings may be taken from the ends of the crest, ensuring the surface cuts are allowed to dry for several days before treating as a normal cutting.

Echeveria akontiophylla

Plants distributed under this name are *E. subalpina.*

Echeveria alata   Alexander

A shrubby plant with erect branches from the base leaves not at all rosulate and scattered along the length of the branches, leaves dark green in summer with red margins 5–6cm. long, 2cm. wide. The flowering stem is a raceme, with bright scarlet flowers, coloured creamy yellow inside, petal tips recurved.

Locality: The mountains in the State of Oaxaca.

Propagation: From stem cuttings.

Echeveria albicans   Walther
Echeveria elegans v kesselringiana   von Poel

Considered at one time to be a variety of *E. elegans* which it resembles, von Poellnitz named it var. *kesselringiana,* a name associated with cacti but not found among the other succulents. Walther's material was supplied to him by Ferd Schmoll of Mexico without definite details of locality. Plants available in Europe originate from Ritter's type plant FR. 532 of which seed was offered by H. Winter, Frankfurt in 1932. After comparisons with sample material received from Europe and Mexico, Walther found the plants identical and formed the opinion that this was an independent species and not a variety.

Albicans signifies white coloured, for which the leaves through good cultivation are lighter than *E. elegans* with a narrower transparent leaf margin. The leaves are also thicker, less in number and end with a slender point often split or forked. They are so glaucous pruinose as to be pale green, almost white. Freely off-setting, the stemless rosettes grow not larger than 10cm. thus this plant is smaller than *E. elegans*. The inflorescence is a simple raceme with cup- or urn-shaped flowers coloured old-rose at the base changing to a light yellow green at the apex.

Propagation: By offsets or leaf cuttings.

Echeveria alpina   Walther

This is a stemless, clump-forming species, with small rosettes. The many truncate leaves blue in colour devoid of any reddish tinge are thinnish, 73mm. long, 30mm. broad, inflorescence is rather short with 10 or more reddish orange flowers.

Locality: Penas de Tomaxco, Puebla Mexico at a height of 3,500m.

Echeveria amoena   De Smet

This charming little plant has been in collections now for over 100 years, and it is so easy to grow and propagates so readily that its virtues are often overlooked. It forms very short stems with so many offsets that a mat is quickly formed of blue pruinose leaves sometimes tinged with pink in spring when dry. The leaves are oblong-spatulate 20mm. long, 7mm. wide, faintly brown at the extreme tip. The flower scapes are cymes with orange flowers.

Locality: Vera Cruz, Mexico.

Propagation: By offsets or leaf cuttings.

Echeveria amphoralis   Walther

This is a small, sub-shrubby species described by Walther (*American Cactus and Succulent Journal*) in 1958. It is found in

Mexico in the province of Oaxaco. It reaches a height of 8in. or more with numerous ascending branches. The puberulous leaves do not form a definite rosette but are somewhat scattered. The leaves are obovate-cuneate in shape, about 3cm. long and just under 2cm. wide. They are bright green in colour tinged with russet. Several inflorescences are produced from below the leaves, having green calyxes and scarlet corollas edged with lemon yellow.

We have not found it to be one of the easiest species in cultivation here as it tends to form a tall unbranched stem although Walther describes it as a good garden plant. According to Walther it is close to *E. harmsii*, having rather large flowers and simple trichomes. Its most attractive characteristic is the colouring of the leaves in full sun.

Echeveria atropurpurea   Baker
       Echeveria sanguinea   Morren

This species eventually forms a stem up to 20cm. high with a rosette of copper red, boat-shaped leaves at the top. The leaves may be up to 15cm. long and 5cm. wide. Best plants are produced from leaf cutting which invariably produce clumps, single plants seldom offsetting. If grown in full sun specimens quickly lose their intense copper red colour by the bleaching effect of the sun's rays, so partial shading during summer by placing below larger specimen plants is advisable. The flower scape is a multilateral raceme of red flowers. It is generally accepted that this species is Mexican in origin, but the definite locality is unknown.

Propagation: By leaf cuttings.

Echeveria australis   Rose

A tropical species that requires a higher winter temperature than the majority of plants in the genus. It forms a tall, many-branched stem up to 30cm. high with the leaves in dense rosettes at the tips of the branches. Leaves are somewhat spoon shaped grey-green slightly pruinose, tinged red when dry in winter, and the flower scape is paniculate with intense small red flowers.

Locality: Central America from the Costa Rica to Panama.

Propagation: For best results from stem cuttings, the leaves are too thin and quickly dry out for any success with leaf cuttings.

Echeveria bella   Alexander

This is a small neat little plant, possessing the smallest rosettes of any known Echeveria species. It has a dense cushion-like appearance due to the many offsets of deep green narrow leaves with reddish tips. It is not easy to grow and almost defies cultivation in this country, under anything less than ideal conditions. In winter it is prone to mildew, unless the atmosphere is kept quite dry. Best results we find are given if the plants are potted in a no-soil mixture, Levington compost is ideal, with one third coarse sand added. Water must be given very sparingly in winter and plants only watered from the bottom. The inflorescence is tall for the size of plant, 10 to 20cm. high, erect, flowers orange-yellow flushed rosy scarlet at the base, they are small in keeping with the size of plant but are produced in profusion. Related to *E. gracilis* they are found near San Cristobal Las Casas, Chiapas, Mexico.

Propagation: By removing and rooting up the abundant offsets in spring.

Echeveria bicolor   (Humb.)   Walther
        Echeveria subspicata   (Baker)   Berger
        Echeveria venezuelensis   Rose
        Sedum bicolor   Humboldt
        Cotyledon subspicata   Baker

This is a shrubby, branching species reaching a height of 30cm. The leaves are in elongated rosettes at the ends of the stems. The lanceolate-spatulate leaves are hardly tapering, the young ones being a shining, light green whilst the older ones are reddish, curved downwards. The flower scape is a 10–12 flowered raceme with red flowers. The plant is found in Venezuela near Caracas, also in Columbia near Bogota. A plant from Sucre, Mexico has been named the variety *turumiquirensis* but considering the distance involved it may be a separate species.

The species is not in commerce but a plant collected for us near Caracas is undoubtedly this species. A plant being distributed under this name is certainly *E. carnicolor*.

Echeveria bifida   Schlecht

This name is given by Jacobsen as a synonym for *E. trianthina* (Rose). The plant however is distributed by Abbey Gardens, a leading U.S.A. nursery, as *E. bifida,* so that apparently the name change is not generally recognised. The plant distributed by Abbey Gardens corresponds to Jacobsen's description of *E. trianthina.*

Echeveria bifida x coccinea   natural hybrid

This plant is included here instead of with the other hybrids as it was collected in the wild and so might well have been taken for a species.

Young plants form a low rosette of narrow, pointed, tomentose leaves, grey green in colour. They are almost identical with young plants of the hybrid Crassula Royal Purple. These two plants are a perfect example of "parallel development" and should serve as a warning to anyone inclined to name a plant without seeing it in flower.

With age a stout stem is formed but with a cluster of sessile rosettes round the base. As the leaves age they take on red colour. The inflorescence starts high up on the stem and at this stage the influence of *E. coccinea* is very evident. The individual flowers are however very different and indicate *E. bifida*, being large and reddish, distributed along the scape instead of crowded together as in *E. coccinea*. The scape is well furnished with bracts, small editions of the rosette leaves, bright red in colour. Flowers appear in late winter.

Echeveria byrnesii   Rose
    Echeveria secunda v. byrnesii   (Rose)   von Poellnitz

This differs from *E. secunda* in having light green, often reddish leaves instead of grey pruinose ones.
Locality: The Volcano of Toluca, Mexico State.
Propagation: From leaf cuttings by removal of offsets.

Echeveria calycosa   Moran

An interesting little species only discovered in 1965 by Uhl near Uruapan, Mexico. The rosettes are rather flat and up to 10cm. in diameter, the leaves light green, and spatulate. The floral stems, at first nodding later become erect, usually with a solitary cincinnus, and the flower is yellow suffused pink at the base.
Locality: On nearly vertical rock faces and steep bank near Uruapan, Mexico.
Propagation: Difficult.

Echeveria campanulata   Kunze

This name is a synonym for *E. grandifolia.* Haw.

Echeveria chihuahuaensis   von Poellnitz

This is a beautiful little species with a dense rosette of leaves only about 4cm. long, greyish white in colour with red edges. It rarely offsets but can be propagated from leaves which will occasionally produce clumps. The inflorescence is a cyme with few flowers, red in colour.

Locality: Chihuahua, in the valley of the Rio Colorado, Mexico.

Propagation: By leaf cuttings.

Echeveria chihuahuaensis. cv. Ruby Blush   Hort.

This cultivar was distributed by the American I.S.I. The typical plant has a grey pruinose rosette with red edges whilst the cultivar has the red more pronounced. Actually we can see little between the two forms which may of course be due to cultivation.

Of the two we find the cultivar far easier and more vigorous. Here again this may be due to differences in the constitution of individual plants. Just as some humans are more vigorous and healthy than others so it is with plants of the same species. To those collectors who are short of space we would suggest that the type and cultivar are so close that there is little point in growing both.

Propagation: By leaf cuttings.

Echeveria carnicolor   (Baker)   Morren

One of the most attractive species. As the name implies, the leaves are flesh coloured, semi transluscent, the leaf surface rather coarse with a crystalline appearance, leaves reflexed at the base of the rosette. Plants forming low mounds by offsetting, and the branched flower scape is about 25cm. high with deep pink flowers in winter. Must be watered from the base or rot soon sets in due to water becoming lodged between the rosette and the top of the soil in the pot. Plants variable in size between 8cm. and 12cm. depending on the clone, and at least two different ones are known, the smaller being considered the most desirable because of its neater appearance, the larger clone easier to cultivate.

Locality: The State of Vera Cruz, Mexico.

Propagation: By leaf cuttings. Offsets, leaf cuttings, may also be taken from the flower scape.

Echeveria chilonensis   Walther

Echeveria whitei   Rose

This is a low branching shrub with twigs about 5cm. long. The leaves are in loose rosettes at the ends of the twigs. The green leaves are oblanceolate-elongate and tapering. The flower scape is a multilateral raceme with yellow flowers.

Locality: It is found at Chilon in Bolivia. The typical plant does not seem to be in cultivation in England but see under *E. whitei.*

Echeveria ciliata   Moran

A small unusual plant with dense rosettes of smooth dark green leaves with fringed margins, first collected by Moran in November 1957 from cliffs near Tamazulapan, Oaxaca, Mexico. The amount of leaf hairs is variable but is mainly confined to the margins and keel, upper surface almost bare, rosettes usually solitary but offsetting in older plants occur, stem short. The inflorescence is a cincinnus, flowers scarlet at the base, the lower half dandelion yellow, interior yellow, gradually becoming orange then scarlet throughout flowering late spring. Related to Echeveria setosa.

Locality: Type plants. East facing cliff at 2100m. elevation above the Mexico-Oaxaca highway 13$\frac{1}{2}$km. north west of Tamazulapan, Oaxaca, Mexico.

Propagation: From leaf cuttings and off sets.

Echeveria coccinea (Cav)   De Candolle

Type species, shrubby, reaching height of 60cm. Some forms are reluctant to branch but others form nice bushy specimens.

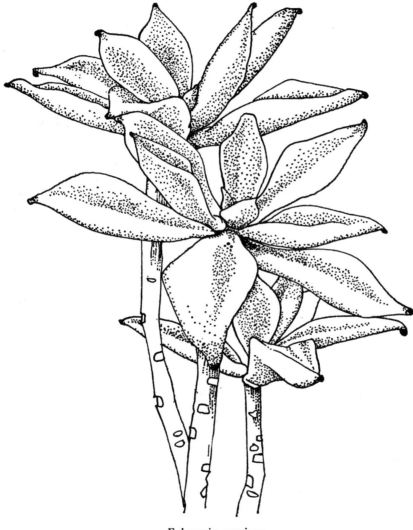

Echeveria coccinea

The leaves form loose rosettes at the ends of the branches. They are green, covered with fine hairs and are lanceolate-spatulate

43

with upper surface convex. The stems are also covered with short fine hair, changing colour from a light silver green below the rosette, through light silver mahogany to an ash grey, stems woody with age. The flower scape is a spike up to a foot high with numerous reddish yellow flowers crowded together.

Locality: Catherina Mountains, Hildalgo, Mexico.

Propagation: Stem cuttings.

Echeveria coccinea 'Recurvata' Hort.

This curiosity has the habitat of the type plant, but shorter wider leaves that are reflexed and twisted to hug the stem. At the time of writing our comparatively recent import is much greener than older typical plants and lacks the fine hairs on the leaves.

Echeveria columbiana von Poellnitz

A South American species forming a small shrub with leaves in a rosette at the ends of the branches. These are obovate wedge shaped, rounded at the tip and only about an inch long. The colour glabrous blue-green with a brown tip, branching freely at the base. Flower scape is a raceme with about ten yellow flowers.

Locality: From the Eastern Cordilleras of Columbia.

Propagation: Stem cuttings.

Echeveria craigiana Walther

An unusual coloured species, rosette up to 10cm. in diameter of ash brown, slightly pruinose leaves, thick at the base, upturned spatulate, rosette usually solitary branching with age. Stem short, thick for the size of the rosette. Flower scape is stout upright with numerous short branches, flowers pink outside, red inside.

Locality: Chihuahua, Mexico.

Propagation: By leaf cuttings in March.

Echeveria crenulata   Rose

This species forms a short, thick stem surmounted by a rosette of very large leaves. These are broadly obovate, narrowing into a stalk towards the base. They are pale green or grey with red margins. The edges are wavy.

The very stout flower scape may be 3ft. high, terminating in a few flowered raceme. The yellowish red flowers have longish pedicels.

It is found in the Mexican State of Morelos.

Echeveria cuspidata   Rose

This species is stemless, having a dense rosette of up to 100 leaves. These are obovate, the upper half being triangular and ending in a pronounced cusp. They are glabrous, pruinose and pale blue in colour. The margin of the upper part of the leaf and the cusp are reddish purple.

The inflorescence has two racemes bent to one side, with purple flowers.

This species comes from the Mexican State of Coahuila. Its culture presents no difficulties. By virtue of the shape of the leaves it is a most distinct species which should be more widely grown.

Echeveria dactylifera   Walther

This is one of the largest species of the genus, rosettes of loose large pointed leaves bright red in colour when grown correctly, leaves convexted to appear almost folded lengthwise.

Locality: Durango, Mexico on high cliffs.

Propagation: Rare in this country, it does not offset, but can be grown from leaves.

Echeveria derenbergii   J. A. Purpus

Common in cultivation and produced by the trade in many thousands annually. Usually stemless globular 8cm. rosettes forming a short stem with age but numerous offsets produced from between the leaves quickly hide this for the plant to form a cushion, leaves broadly spatulate, overlaid with white-grey pruinose, ending in a short reddish brown point, the colour extending to the margins. The flower scape is a curved short raceme with reddish orange flowers.

Locality: Oaxaca, Mexico.

Propagation: By leaf cuttings or offsets, leaf cuttings producing the best plants.

Echeveria elegans   Rose
Echeveria perelegans   Berger

The name of this plant, which means choice or neat is an apt description for this popular species, which forms a dense pale blue rosette 10cm. in diameter, leaves upturned, pointed, thick strongly pruinose with transparent margins. With good cultivation the tips faintly blushed with pink on the reverse side of the older leaves in winter. It is stemless but forms offsets on elongated stolons which appear from below the main rosette when mature, and eventually a cushion is formed. The flower spike is a curved raceme with pink tipped yellow bells appearing in summer.

Locality: Penas de Jacal, near Pachuca Hidalgo, Mexico.

Propagation: By offsets or leaf cuttings.

Echeveria excelsa   (Diels)   Berger
Cotyledon excelsa   Diels

On a visit to Peru, Mr. Maurice Mason collected a number of Echeveria from a restricted area. Leaves were most variable both in shape and colour but it is probable that they were all forms of a very variable species. In the stemless rosettes of obovate-wedge shaped, tapering leaves, long and relatively narrow they correspond to descriptions of *E. excelsa*. Leaf colour was usually grey-green, sometimes tinged purple. Flowers were not seen.

Echeveria expatriata   Rose

This plant has never been collected and the habitat is not known, appropriately the name means "out of the country". Shooting freely from the base, this species soon fills a pan with its 4in. long (10cm.) weak stems, each with a leaf rosette at the tip. The oblanceolate leaves, about 1in. long (2½cm.) are convex on both sides and are pale grey-green pruinose. The slight flower scape is a few flowered cyme with small reddish flowers.

Echeveria fimbriata   C. H. Thomps

This species belongs to the "gibbiflora" group and is a very handsome plant. With age it forms a stout, tall stem crowned by a rosette of large, spatulate leaves whose margins are fringed. The colour is a blend of blue, pink and mauve. The inflorescence is a tall, many flowered raceme, with red yellow tipped flowers. *Locality:* Cuernavaca, Mexico.

Echeveria fulgens   Lemaire
Echeveria retusa   Lindley

This is particularly valuable as it flowers freely in winter. It has stems up to 15cm. high, often branched, topped by a rosette of large spatulate leaves broad at the base, light blue-green in colour with reddish margins and only slightly pruinose. The tall stout flower scape is an irregular panicle often branched, flowers red outside and yellow inside. The flower scape often grows at the expense of the rosette which reduces considerably in size until the plant has completed flowering, this does not appear detrimental in any-way, as it quickly recovers during late spring and early summer when an occasional feed at this time will be found beneficial.

Locality: Michogan, Mexico.

Propagation: By seed as it is self fertile, or cuttings.

Echeveria gibbiflora   De Candolle

This is a tall stout-growing species, seldom branching. The stem is bare except for the rosette of up to 20 leaves at the top. The leaves, up to 25cm. long, oblong-spatulate, basally keeled and concave above, are light grey-green flushed red. Recently J. W. Dodson has discovered a particularly variable population of the species about 40 miles from Mexico City. Some of the individual plants approaching closely to the purplish leaved *E. violescens.* The flower scape, up to 60cm. high, is a branched panicle with light red flowers in winter. It, with its varieties, is best beheaded and re-rooted at intervals of two to four years as, with age, the size of the rosettes tend to deteriorate. To maintain a large rosette, a reasonably rich compost should be used with an occasional summer feed.

Locality: South of Mexico City, Mexico.

Propagation: By cuttings, the stump after removing the rosette will throw out side shoots which should be removed as soon as large enough. Occasionally by leaf cuttings, but these will invariably root without forming plantlets.

Echeveria gibbiflora v. 'Carunculata'   Hort.

This plant is unusual with its gibbous protuberances on the upper surface of the mature leaves giving a cameo effect. Leaves are not in the close rosette of the type and some are distributed down the stem. Leaf-colours are delicate pastel shades of pink and lavender pruinose which extends to the unbranched stem.

New leaves in spring are usually plain without carunculations, but this reappears again on early summer growth, flower scape similar to the type, flowers smaller, pink, yellow inside at the throat. Lack of water during spring and summer causes withering of the leaf tips.

33 *Echeveria pallida*

34 'Rubella'

35 'Silveron Red'

36 *Echeveria affinis*

37 'Gypsy'

38 *Echeveria harmsii*

39 'Mary Butterfield'

40 'Purpurea'

41 *Echeveria runyonii*
Inflorescence

42 *Echeveria nodulosa*

43 *Echeveria sedoides*

44 *Echeveria multicaulis*

45 *Echeveria atropurpurea*

46 'Bittersweet'

47 Gilva cv. 'Blue Surprise'

48 A mixed collection of Echeveria

Locality: Never collected.

Propagation: Can be propagated by removal of side shoots taken off the main stem after removing or beheading the rosette. The stump has an annoying way of drying up from the top, so the side shoots should be removed as soon as possible.

Leaves from the inflorescence can be used as leaf cuttings or the inflorescence can be cut into sections each with a leaf attached and these can be planted as cuttings. This method is not always successful and this variety will always remain uncommon due to the difficulties of propagation.

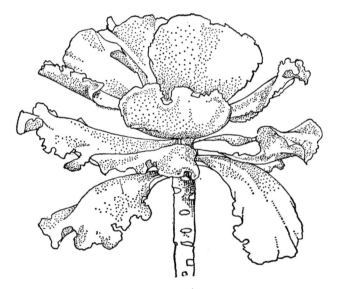

Echeveria gibbiflora var Crispata

Echeveria gibbiflora var. crispata   Baker

Similar to the type but has crenate or wavy margins to the leaves.

Echeveria gibbiflora var. metallica   (Lem.)   Baker

Has leaves more rounded at the tips. They are more pruinose, bronze coloured and with reddish margins. The name is sometimes given to *E. violescens.*

Echeveria gigantea   Rose et Purp

This plant is well named with stout stems in clumps over a foot high terminating in massive leaf rosettes. The leaves are up to 22cm. long, obovate-lanceolate becoming narrow and very fleshy at the base. They are light green or grey-pruinose with an intense red margin.

The flower scape may reach a height of 6ft. with a branching panicle of flesh-red flowers.

Its habitat is the Mexican State of Puebla.

For proper development a rich soil is needed.

Echeveria glauca   Baker

This is a very well-known species largely used for summer bedding displays and as edging plants. It is practically hardy provided it is kept dry. It is stemless, forming numerous offsets. The obovate-spatulate leaves are glaucous blue, with reddish margins when older. The flower scape is a long, thin raceme bent over at the top, with red flowers.

Locality: Distrito Federal, Mexico and Santa Fé Valley, Mexico.

Propagation: From offsets and leaf cuttings.

Echeveria glauca var. pumila (Schlecht)   von Poellnitz

Differs from the type in having narrower and longer leaves and flowers tipped red. There are also cristate and variegated forms.

Echeveria glauca. var. metallica   Hort.

Similar to type, leaves flushed pink during early spring.

Echeveria goldmanii Rose

Named after Edward A. Goldman, it is a bushy species, reaching a height of 20cm., erect when young but later becomes procumbent, the branches rooting in contact with the soil. The leaves are loosely arranged and do not form rosettes. They are narrow and blunt, shining light green with a red margin. The inflorescence is a multilateral raceme with reddish flowers.

Echeveria goldmanii

Locality: Comitan, Chiapas, Mexico.

Propagation: By cuttings taken from the tips of the many branches.

Echeveria gracillima   Muhlenpf

The status of this plant has not been strictly defined. It may be a variety or form or even a hybrid of *E. secunda* (Booth).

It differs from *E. secunda* in having narrower, more pointed leaves and smaller flowers.

Echeveria grandifolia   Haw
E. campanulata   Kunze

This species may well be one of the parents of the many hybrids now originating in the U.S.A. and has a general similarity to many of them.

A rosette of large leaves is carried at the top of a tall, thick stem. The leaves are spatulate, thickened at the base and finally cylindrically narrowed. They are glabrous, intensely grey pruinose edged with pink.

The thickened flower scape may reach a height of over 2ft. with a panicle of flowers on its upper third. These are reddish with a yellow interior.

Locality: Mexican State of Guerrero.

Echeveria guatemalensis   Rose

This is a shrubby, clump-forming species reaching a height of 15cm. or more. The leaves are not rosulate but alternate at the tips of the branches. They are spatulate, tapering, broadly stalked and spreading at right angles to the stem. They are green with reddish margins. The flower spike has a multilateral raceme with reddish-yellow flowers.

Locality: This is a Central American species first found on the Volcano of Agua in Guatemala.

Echeveria halbingeri   Walther

This is a very attractive plant, one of the smallest of the genus.

It is quite stemless and only offsets with age, and eventually almost a cushion is formed.

The rosette is crowded with turgid, obovate leaves only 2cm. long which terminate in a short reddish point. They are slightly pruinose and bluish-green in colour. The corolla is urceolate-campanulate, petal tips being out-curved, orange-rufous outside, pale orange inside. These recurved petal tips distinguish it from allied species. Its locality is said to be Hidalgo, Mexico.

Propagation: By removal of the many offsets produced on mature plants and treating them as cuttings.

Echeveria harmsii   Macbride
Cotyledon elegans   N. E. Brown
Oliveranthus elegans   Rose

A favourite species by florists and sold in quantity as a house plant. It forms a small branched sub-shrub. The leaves are crowded at the tips of the branches. They are lanceolate, about 30cm. long, green tipped brown, and covered with soft hairs. The flowers are usually solitary and 3cm. long, quite the largest in the genus, and they are bright scarlet with a lighter tip.

Locality: Mexico.
Propagation: Stem cuttings.

Echeveria humilis   Rose

When not in flower and as a young plant, this species appears very similar to *E. craigiana,* the leaves not as upturned. The name means "low growing".

The inflorescence in this case is a slender cincinnus with orange flowers, having sepals standing out at right angles to the stem of a peculiar gun-metal colour.

When in flower there is no possibility of confusing the two species, both flowering in late summer.

Locality: San Luis Potosi, Mexico.
Propagation: From leaf cuttings.

Echeveria heterosepala   Rose

        Echeveria viridiflora   Rose

        Pachyphytum chloranthum   Walther

        Pachyphytum heterosepalum   Walther

Whilst sometimes included in Pachyphytum it is aberrant to that genus and is best placed in Echeveria. It has a stem up to 5cm. high with a rosette of lanceolate leaves yellowish-green tinged red. The erect inflorescence carries numerous flowers light green in colour, the tips of the petals spreading. Strong light and moderate watering are needed to keep the growth compact, but we find it one of the more difficult species.

Locality: Found growing among rubble on a gentle slope near Zapotitlan, Puebla, Mexico.

Echeveria hyalina   Walther

This species forms a stemless rosette, only offsetting rarely when mature, somewhat less than 13cm. in diameter. The leaves are rather thin, with a hyaline margin. They are obovate, cuneate, ending in a short cusp, pale-bluish white with a crystalline texture.

The inflorescence is a simple raceme, with the flowering portion drooping. The urceolate corolla is old rose below, pale flesh-colour above and light green at the tip with a green interior.

Its locality is unknown, apart from Mexico.

Propagation: Not known.

Echeveria johnsonii   Walther

This is a small shrubby species with rather weak stems that may become decumbent. The leaves are not rosulate but crowded along the upper ends of the branches. They are linear-oblong, obtuse and minutely apiculate. They are medium green with purple coloration along the edges near the apex. The short inflorescence is sub-spicate, the flowers having a coral red exterior and yellowish interior.

Locality: This is a plant of the northern Andes, from Ecuador into Columbia, from where our plants were collected.

Echeveria juarezensis   Walther

This recently discovered species has a loose rosette on top of a bare stem and has a strong resemblance to some species of Aeonium. The leaves are blue-green with red margins spreading over a greater area of the leaves as they age. They are spatulate, tapering towards the base, the upper surface strongly concave, lower surface with a keel.

Our plants have not yet flowered.

Echeveria longipes   Walther

This species has a short, subterranean stem with a rosette of glabrous, linear, very acute leaves, six times as long as wide. They are pale green with a grey pruinose coating.

The inflorescence is racemose-paniculate. The branches mostly carry only one flower. This has a flesh coloured exterior and yellow interior.

Locality: It occurs in the mountains between Puebla and Oaxaca and can be confused with *E. paniculata.*

Echeveria leucotricha   Purpus

Firstly described in 1914 this species has become a rarity in advanced collections, slow growing. This is a sub-shrub with branches ending in a loose rosette about 15cm. in diameter.

The lanceolate leaves end in a blunt tip and are densely covered with silvery white hair except at the tip where it is brown. This gives it a superficial resemblance to *Kalanchoe tomentosa.* The flowers are cinnabar red. Glass, in the *American Journal*, states that this is an exceedingly difficult species requiring half shade in summer. This is not our experience as, grown in full sun in England, its cultivation offers no difficulty.

Its locality is San Luis Tulilanopa, Sierra de Mixteca, Puebla, Mexico.

Propagation: Will not grow from leaf cuttings. These if taken will root but not throw plantlets. Only from stem cuttings.

Echeveria lutea   Rose

One of the most outstanding species in the genus. It is usually stemless, and has a rosette of almost linear leaves less than 5cm. long and about 1cm. wide, folded almost double. They are yellowish-green heavily tinged with reddish-brown. The inflorescence is a single cincinnus with numerous bracts resembling the rosette leaves but getting smaller towards the top. The flowers are unusual in the genus by being bright buttercup yellow.

Its locality is over a fairly wide range in the San Luis Potosi, Mexico, where it grows on limestone on eastern exposures.

It is somewhat variable. Plants from Hidalgo have grey-green leaves and the yellow flowers are tipped orange.

Propagation: From leaf cuttings.

Echeveria macdougallii   Walther

This species must not be confused with *Graptopetalum macdougalli* but apart from the name the two have nothing in common.

It is a small sub-shrub only about 15cm. high with numerous spreading branches giving an ungainly effect for an Echeveria. The leaves do not form rosettes but are closely spaced along the upper parts of the twigs. The leaves are oblong-obovate, much thickened and keeled, little more than 2cm. long and bluntly pointed. They are mid-green tinged dull red along the edges.

The infloresence is spreading and forms a short raceme. The few flowers are peach-red outside and chrome yellow inside.

The locality is in the Mexican State of Oaxaca.

Echeveria maculata   Rose

This forms a fairly large stemless rosette with lanceolate leaves 10cm. long and about 2cm. wide. The dark green leaves are somewhat mottled, hence the name. The stout flowering stem may be over 60cm. high. The paniculate inflorescence has 3 or 4 sessile flowers on the lower branches arranged along the side of the branch but the upper flowers are axillary and sessile. They are pale lemon yellow.

The species comes from Hidalgo, Mexico.

The plant grown here under this name was collected by Foster and Glass, No. 1989. It differs from the above description by lacking the mottling on the leaves. Besides forming offsets from the base the central rosette has split into two.

Echeveria maxonii   Rose

A shrubby species which forms stems that eventually reach 70cm. in length. Whilst young plants are erect, the long stems become prostrate. The leaves are loosely arranged along the stem becoming more crowded at the tips. They are spatulate-obtuse, narrowed to form stalks, green with reddish margins.

The flower scape is a raceme with salmon-coloured flowers. Unlike the majority of species cultivated here it comes from Guatemala, not Mexico. Between Salama and Los Canvas near Zimil, Quezaltenango, Chuacuo.

Propagation: From stem cuttings.

Echeveria megacalyx   Walther

This species does not flourish here to the same extent as other Echeverias, possibly due to the thin leaves, which necessitates more watering than other varieties. The stem is short with a dense rosette of nearly flat, oblong spatulate, up or recurved leaves. These are dark bluish glaucous. The inflorescence is spicate, strongly curved at the apex. The urn-shaped corolla is dull greenish yellow with sepals the colour of the leaves.

Its locality is on rocks high in the pine forests of Oaxaca, Mexico.

Propagation: Stem cuttings in spring.

Echeveria microcalyx

Echeveria microcalyx   Britton/Rose

This species has lax, branched stems up to 10cm. long. When mature they hang over the sides of the pot but the terminal rosettes turn upwards. The stems are well furnished with loosely attached leaves, and these are spatulate, tapering about 25mm. long, glaucous blue with a pink tinge. The paniculate inflorescence carries a few smallish, yellow-red flowers.

Its locality is Pueblo and Vera Cruz, Mexico.

Propagation: From stem cuttings or leaf cuttings.

Echeveria mucronata (Baker)   Schlechtendahl
         Cotyledon mucronata Baker

This has leaves in stemless rosettes, narrow spatulate, pointed and green in colour. The rosettes may be up to 20cm. in diameter. The inflorescence is a multilateral spike with reddish-yellow flowers. This is one of the less distinctive species.

Its locality is Central Mexico.

Propagation: From offsets and leaf cuttings.

Echeveria multicaulis   Rose

A shrubby plant with stiff woody stems reaching a height of 20cm. Stems terminate in dense rosettes but carry leaves along much of their length. The leaves are broadly obovate, rounded at the ends. They are glossy green with reddish margins when old.

The inflorescence is a densely flowered raceme with comparatively large reddish flowers having yellowish interiors, flowering period January/February.

Its locality is in the state of Guerrero, Mexico.

Propagation: Stem cuttings in spring.

Echeveria moranii   Walther

This somewhat temperamental plant forms a close rosette of many leaves. Leaves are oblanceolate, about twice as long as wide and nearly as thick as wide. They are yellowish-green with

59

a mahogany tip and margin. The keel along the lower surface of the leaf is also mahogany.

Plant is still to flower.

Echeveria nodulosa (Baker) Otto
Echeveria sturmiana von Poellnitz

This species is a sparsely branched shrub, up to 50cm. high. The rosettes are usually rather lax and stems are reasonably well furnished with leaves.

The leaves are broadly acute to rounded, with three low ridges. Minute papilae given them a somewhat whitish appearance when viewed obliquely and they are heavily marked with purplish red along the margin and keel. In some forms there are reddish marks on one or both surfaces.

The floral stems are tall, with smallish flowers rather widely spaced. The flowers are pale yellow suffused with red from the base.

Its locality is Mt. Alba, Oaxaca, growing on gravelly hillsides either in the open or under brush, sometimes in deep shade, so unlike most species it should not be grown in full sun.

Propagation: Usually from stem cuttings, leaf cuttings can be taken but they are slow to grow to any size.

Echeveria nuda Lindley

A fast growing species which rapidly forms stems up to 60cm. high. These are erect and more or less branching. Leaves are only crowded into rosettes at the tips of the stems, older leaves being scattered. The rosette leaves are dull green, with or without a purplish red margin.

The inflorescence is a raceme, erect from the beginning. The corolla is geranium red for the lower half, bright yellow above and inside. This is not one of the most attractive species.

Its locality is Orizaba, Vera Cruz, Mexico, on rocks above the highway and is related to other species from Southern Mexico, Central and South America.

Propagation: Stem cuttings.

Echeveria obtusifolia   Rose
        Echeveria scopulorum   Rose

This species has a short stem with leaves in an open rosette. They are obovate, hardly tapering, but much narrowed at the base. In some forms the edges are considerably crimped. They are darkish green and in winter may turn bright red.

It is very floriferous in winter, with many flowered racemes carrying red flowers. In general appearance when flowering it resembles *E. fulgens* of which it is suggested it may be a form. This is one of the better species for winter decoration.

Locality: Is in the Mexican States for Morelos and Mexico.

Propagation: From leaf cuttings which invariably produce clumps.

Echeveria pallida   Walther
Type: California Academy of Sciences No. 251053 (E. Walther 1935)

This striking species has a stout stem and leaves 15cm. by 10cm. broad, and are in loose rosettes, widest near the rounded tips and narrowing to a distinct stalk at the base. The back surface is definitely keeled. The colour is unusual for the genus, pale yellowish-green with a pink margin. There is a stout 50cm. inflorescence, paniculate, branches eight or more with large, pink campanulate flowers. Flowering in winter.

Its exact locality is not known, but Walther's type plant was found in cultivation in Mexico City, and is said to have come from near Cordoba.

Propagation: Mature plants form offsets at the base which when removed can be treated as stem cuttings.

Echeveria paniculate   Gray
        Cotyledon grayi   Baker
        Echeveria grayi   Morren
        Echeveria schaffneri   Rose

This species is stemless with a dense rosette of numerous leaves. These are narrowly lanceolate, five times as long as wide. They are dark green to pale blue-green, often somewhat spotted.

The flower scape is a multilateral raceme or panicle with reddish or pale yellow flowers.

Locality: It is widespread through Chihuahua, Durango and Hidalgo.

Echeveria peacockii

Echeveria peacockii (Baker)		Morren
Echeveria desmetiana	De Smet	
Echeveria subsessilis	Rose	
Echeveria tenuis	Rose	

This stemless plant has a very dense rosette 10cm. diameter. The sub-obovate leaves are sharply pointed and tapering towards the base. Although the leaves are bluish in colour they are so densely pruinose as to appear almost white. Margins and tips are sometimes reddish. The inflorescence is a one sided raceme with intensely red pruinose flowers.

Locality: Its exact habitat is unknown, apart from Mexico.

Propagation: Leaf cuttings do not take, but it may be grown from seed or offsets which appear occasionally on mature plants.

Echeveria pilosa

Purpus

As the name implies, the narrow pointed leaves are covered with white soft hairs except at the tip where it is brown. It has a short stem, branching with age from the base, covered with short brown hair.

The flower scape is likewise hairy, the dull orange flowers being carried in panicles.

Locality: Its habitat is San Luis Tultitlanapo, Sierra de Mixteca, Puebla, Mexico.

Propagation: From cuttings.

Echeveria pittieri

Rose

Echeveria rosea Lindley

A plant grown in England for many years as *E. rosea* is very distinct from the plant under that name grown at Berkeley Gardens, California. Mr. Kimnach of Berkeley suggests that our plant is *E. pittieri*, listed by Walther in 1935 as a synonymy of *E. rosea*.

It is a freely branching sub-shrub with leaves in loose rosettes. They are narrow and tapering, glabrous, pale-green tinged with pink. The inflorescence is a spike with the yellowish flowers closely crowded round it, admixed with pink bracts. As it flowers in winter it is a most desirable plant.

Locality: It is found at Laguna, Volcano of Ipala, Guatemala.

Propagation: From stem cutting.

Echeveria potosina

Walther

Plants we have seen under this name are probably *E. elegans*. The true plants have longer, straighter leaves, very thick and turgid 4–6cm. long and 2–3cm. broad near the apex, of marble-like texture and pale glaucous green in colour with a purplish tinge at the tips.

Rosettes dense, with few or no offsets. A further distinguishing feature is the urceolate flower which is conspicuously green-tipped in bud. It is probably not in cultivation in England.

Locality: Exact habitat is not known, but it was received by Walther from San Luis Potosi and presumed indigenous to that part of Mexico. Type specimen California Academy of Sciences No. 223896.

Propagation: Not known but its similarity to *elegans* indicates it could possibly be propagated by leaf cuttings.

Echeveria pringlei (S. Watson)   Rose

This species has a long, prostrate hairy stem. The leaves are in loose rosettes and are oblanceolate, 5–10cm. long. They are a somewhat sickly looking yellowish green. The flowers are an intense red. For good cultivation this species requires more frequent watering.

Locality: It is found at Baranca near Guadalajara, Jalisco, Mexico.

Propagation: Stem cuttings in spring.

Echeveria procera   Moran

This plant is one of the tallest growing of the genus. Although it was discovered as long ago as 1947 by Mr. T. McDougall, it is not as yet available to us in England. It grows up to 2m. tall, stems 3–4cm. thick usually solitary, sparsely branching, topped by a loose rosette of 20–30 leaves, which are glaucous green at first, with narrow red margins, and are up to 10cm. long and 4–6cm. wide, rounded to slightly retuse at the tip. The inflorescence is a stout spike carrying 30–50 or more light red flowers which have a light yellow interior.

Locality: At La Muralla at the summit of Cerro Yucunino, 3,300m. (about 10 miles) south of Tlaxiaco, State of Oaxaca, Mexico.

Propagation: Not yet known.

Echeveria pulchella Berger

This species forms cushions of stemless, dense rosettes of glabrous, sap-green leaves. Leaves are obovate-spatulate with the upper surface flat and keeled underneath. The inflorescence is a slightly nodding cyme, with light red flowers.

Locality: It comes from Mexico, habitat not given.

Propagation: From stem cuttings.

Echeveria pulidonis Walther

An interesting new species, the name of which as far as we know has not yet been validly published. It is a handsome small Echeveria with compact 10cm. diameter rosettes of greenish, red bordered leaves. It differs from all other species except *E. lutea* in having golden yellow flowers.

Locality: Its habitat in Puebla, Mexico.

Propagation: Grown quite easily from leaf cuttings taken in spring.

Echeveria pulvinata Rose
Cotyledon pulvinata Hooker

The name is descriptive of the leaves, which means pillow-shaped. It is a sub-shrub with the leaves thickly felted usually silvery in colour but sometimes brownish with age. Leaves are obovate, half as wide as long with a short tip.

The rosettes are loose and the flower stems come out horizontally from among the lower leaves. The red flowers appear in early spring.

Locality: The Tommelin Canyon, Oaxaca, Mexico.

Propagation: From stem cuttings. Leaf cuttings taken will root but will seldom form a new plantlet.

Echeveria pulvinata c.v. 'Ruby' Boom

This cultivar being much more attractive than the type with

its much narrower leaves with red hair on the margins and the tip, is usually offered as *E. pulvinata.* The type species seldom being propagated commercially.

Propagation: As the type.

Echeveria purpusorum   Berger
Urbinia purpusii   Rose

This plant has a stemless rosette of grey-green, red spotted leaves triangular ovate in shape and keeled at the back. The flowers, like all the former Urbinias are globose, red and yellow.

Locality: It is found in Southern Mexico.

Propagation: From offsets and leaf cuttings, although the leaves are difficult to remove.

Echeveria racemosa   Schelcht/Chamisso
Echeveria lurida   Howarth

Described by Howarth in Taylor's *Philosophical Magazine* 1831 which had been described by Chamisso one year previously as *Echeveria racemosa* in Linnea V. 554, confusion between these two names persists.

This is stemless with narrow lanceolate leaves in a dense rosette. The leaves have a finely cartilaginous edge and are reddish in colour but being grey pruinose the final effect is plum colour. The flower scape is very tall for the size of the rosette. It is a raceme with pale orange flowers.

Locality: Vera Cruz, Mexico.

Propagation: Leaf cuttings.

Echeveria rauschii   van Keppel

This somewhat variable species may have a short, stout erect stem or a thin, longer decumbent one branching at the base. The oblong-oblanceolate leaves are a fresh green with a red mucro and dark red margins.

The inflorescence is a single raceme. The erect flowers are orange to yellow with green sepals.

It grows in humus-filled hollows on steep slopes north of Sucre, Bolivia. Its chief difference from *E. vanvlietii* is the inflorescence whose flowers are horizontal or ascending instead of drooping.

Echeveria rosea   Lindley

Courantia echeverioides	Lemaire
Cotyledon roseata	Baker
Courantia rosea	Lem.

First described by John Lindley in Edwards's *Botanical Register* in 1842 No. 22. The plant was first imported to England in 1841 by Mssrs. Lee & Co., of the Vineyard, Hammersmith. Sub-titled in his original description "Rosy Echeveria".

As already noted there is some confusion over this plant. Walther considered *E. pittieri*. Rose and *E. rosea* synonymus. A plant supplied by M. Kimnach and van Keppel as *E. rosea* has wider leaves than *E. pittieri*. Leaves blue-green, flushed pink from the tip when older, margins slightly flushed in winter. The inflorescence is also much shorter.

Locality: San Luis Potosi, Vera Cruz and Oaxaca, Mexico.

Propagation: Stem or leaf cuttings.

Echeveria runyonii   Rose

Type specimens U.S. National Herbarium No. 1319920 (Runyon 22/R: 339)

This very attractive species has a short stem with a rosette of rosulate, upcurved leaves. They are spatulate 6–8 cm. long, 3–4cm. broad, flattish with a rounded end, pale blue with a heavy bloom that makes them almost white in appearance. The tall inflorescence is a raceme bifid, curved over at the top and carries salmon pink to scarlet blooms in autumn.

Locality: Known only from cultivated plants found in a Mexican garden at Matamoras.

Propagation: Grows easily from leaf cuttings which produce attractive clumps.

Echeveria runyonii

Echeveria runyonii var. macabeana   Walther
Type specimens California Academy of Sciences No. 223894
(Walther 35/51)

Very similar to type but leaves acute, and the colour is deep grape green, but very glaucous and so appearing a pale medic-blue. Racemes two, curved over at the top and carries pink blooms changing to scarlet.

Locality: Not stated, and not considered a hybrid by Walther.
Propagation: As for type.

Echeveria sanchez-mejoradai   Walther

This is another undescribed species. It is related to *E. elegans* but has narrower and more pointed leaves. Its whitish rosettes turn reddish if grown in full sun and kept dry.
Locality: It was found in the state of Hidalgo, Mexico.
Propagation: From leaf cuttings taken in the spring.

Echeveria sedoides   Walther

This is a shrubby, branching species reaching a height of 20cm. The branches are lax and the leaves scattered, not forming rosettes, so that it looks more like a sedum than an Echeveria. The leaves are oblong-obovate and quite thick, not more than 2cm. long. The inflorescences are upright, equilaterally racemose and few flowered. The corollas are campanulate, with petals sharply keeled at the back, scarlet with chrome edges and apricot interior.

Its locality is only known from a restricted area of Oaxaca, Mexico.

Echeveria secunda   Booth

This species is so close to *E. glauca* that the latter was once considered to be only a variety of it. It is very short-stemmed and offsets freely. The obovate leaves are distinctly acuminate, light green but reddish towards the tips and slightly pruinose. The older leaves of the dense rosettes are ascending. The flower scape is thin, a raceme bent to one side with red, yellow tipped flowers.

Its locality is in the state of Hidalgo, Mexico.
Propagation: From offsets which when removed should be treated as cuttings, but will grow also from leaf cuttings if taken in spring.

Echeveria sessiliflora   Rose

E. corallina   Alexander

This species has a short stem terminating in a loose rosette. The leaves are oblanceolate, shortly tapering. The younger ones are blue and upstanding whilst the older ones are spreading and olive green tinged with red. They may have brownish-red margins but this may be influenced by growing conditions or even by variation within the species.

The inflorescence carries bracts like the leaves but diminishing in size towards the apex. The sessile flowers are multilaterally arranged. They have a blue-green calyx and a coral red corolla.

The habitat is the Mexican State of Chiapas.

The variety *pinetorum* of *v. Poell'n,* has been given specific status by Rose but we have not yet met with it in cultivation here.

Echeveria setosa

70

Echeveria setosa   Rose/Purpus

This popular species is usually stemless and only offsets when mature. It forms a dense, almost flat rosette which may be 15cm. in diameter. The rather narrow leaves are clavate with obtuse apices and convex on both sides. They are dark green and covered with dense white bristly hairs. The inflorescence is of medium height with numerous showy red and yellow flowers in spring. There is also a cristate variety which is not so regular as that of *E. agavoides* and many of the shoots tend to revert to the normal form.

Locality: The mountains in the State of Puebla, Mexico.

Propagation: From leaf cuttings or offsets from mature plants which are treated as cuttings.

Echeveria semivestita (Moran) var. semivestita   Walther

This plant forms a short, unbranched stem with a rosette of narrow oblanceolate leaves, concave above and slightly keeled below. They are dark green, edged with purplish red. The whole plant is puberulent, the inflorescence is paniculate with racemose branches. Flowers are coral pink outside and yellowish or light red inside.

Locality: Its habitat is the state of Hidalgo, Mexico.

Propagation: From leaf cuttings in the spring.

Echeveria semivestita var. floresina   Walther

This plant is similar to type except that it is quite glabrous instead of puberalous.

Echeveria shaviana   Walther

This very beautiful species has only just had the name validly published, but it is now widely known in England due largely to its ease in propagation and the demand for it.

The dense rosettes usually reach 10cm. in diameter and offsets with age, the offsets should be removed so as not to spoil the shape of the plant. The leaves are incurved, the ends crimped with pinkish hyaline margins.

Locality: It occurs on rocks in the pine forests of Tamaulipas, Mexico.

Propagation: Grows quickly and easily from leaf cuttings.

Echeveria shaviana

Echeveria shaviana cv. 'Pink Frills'   Hort.

This cultivar is similar to the type, rosette more open with fewer leaves which are covered with a pink bloom, leaves flatter and less incurved. There is no trace of hybridisation.

Propagation: As for the type.

Echeveria simulans   Rose

This plant is sometimes considered to be a variety of *E. elegans* which it somewhat resembles. The acuminate leaves are longer and narrower, with a stouter mucro. They are silvery in colour. The flowers, red yellowish at the apex are cylindroid instead of urceolate.

Locality: It is found in Monterey, State of Nuevo Leon, Mexico.

Propagation: Leaf cuttings, plants seldom producing offsets.

Echeveria spectabilis   Alexander

This forms a small, branched shrub up to 60cm. **in height.** There is a loose rosette of leaves at the end of each branch but leaves are loosely arranged on the lower parts. The leaves are distinctly stalked and finely papillose all over, and they are yellow-green with a red margin. The tall inflorescence carries lemon yellow flowers in multilateral racemes.

Locality: It is found in Oaxaca, Mexico.

Propagation: From stem cuttings taken from the tips of the branches.

Echeveria strictiflora   Gray

This species is unique in being the only Echeveria native to the United States. Many Californian plants have been named as Echeverias in the past but they have all been transferred to

73

Dudleya. Strangely enough, whilst growing in the most readily accessible habitat it is never offered by nurseries and our plant was specially collected for us on Hall's Half Acre Ranch in Western Texas.

It is stemless and clump forming, densely rosulate. The oblanceolate leaves taper to a long point. They are glabrous, pale blue in colour, with whitish overtones which give it a resemblance to many Dudleyas. The upper surface is deeply concave and the back surface keeled. Jacobsen gives the colour as dark olive, darker towards the base but there is no sign of this on our plant. This, and the leaf shape, indicates some variability.

The flower scape is pink with a multilateral spike and a number of scarcely stalked pink flowers.

Echeveria subalpina   Rose/Purpus
                  Echeveria akontiophylla

This is a stemless plant with leaves in a dense rosette. They are linear-lanceolate, narrowed at the base and terminating in a dark brown, hard tip. The pale green leaves are densely whitish pruinose. The flower scape consists of one or two racemes, curved at the top, with vermillion flowers.

Locality: It is found in mountainous regions of Orizaba, State of Vera Cruz, Mexico.

Propagation: Offsets, which when taken should be treated as cuttings.

Echeveria subrigida (Rob/Seaton)   Rose

This, perhaps the most beautiful species of Echeveria, was first collected by G. G. Pringle in October, 1892 and was subsequently described by Dr. Rose in 1903. It was lost to cultivation and has only, comparatively recently been re-introduced. It is seldom seen in our collections due to difficulty of cultivation, and still more so to propagation.

Its rosette eventually reaches 30cm. in diameter and forms a stem slowly. When over 10cm. high the plant becomes top-heavy and less attractive. It should then be beheaded and re-rooted, the stump forming offsets if properly treated. The leaves are laxly expanded in a whorl, and are lanceolate and thickly covered with white farina, the underlying green epidermis giving a slight bluish cast. Each leaf is bordered with deep pink. The flowers are very large and deep orange, with white powdered bracts and sepals. There are clone variations from the type, one in van Keppel's collection, its lanceolate leaves green complete with its deep pink border. This was collected from habitat and it is not known if the lack of farina was due to being grown in continual shade or from some other cause. Another in our own collection is identical in habit—complete with abundant farina but lacking the distinctive pink border. Certain plants on sale here under this name are obviously inferior hybrids, the leaves being narrower and bluer, and the distinctive border is also much less pronounced, the rosettes seldom growing above 10cm. in diameter with flowers more like *E. glauca*.

A very open compost must be used to prevent stem or root rot, and plants should not be watered from overhead. In winter it should be kept dry.

Locality: Tultenango Canyon, west of Mexico City, Mexico.

Propagation: Leaf cuttings do not take, but hand pollinated seeds can be used for propagation. Care must be taken to prevent cross fertilisation.

Echeveria tobarensis   Berger
Urbinia lurida   Rose

A stemless plant with leaves in a dense rosette, the younger leaves somewhat erect. They are ovate, tapering to a point, and quite thick, coloured a purple or dull red and quite glabrous.

The tall flower scapes are racemes, too thin to stand erect and carry globular red and yellow flowers.

Locality: They are found in the State of Durango, Mexico.

Propagation: From leaf cuttings taken in the spring.

Echeveria tolimanense Matuda

This is a species from the Mexican province of Hidalgo where it grows on the cliffs of the Barrance de Toliman, hence its name. In general appearance it is close to *E. craigiana* with thick rounded leaves more like a Pachyphytum than an Echeveria. It is stemless, with a dense rosette of ash-grey leaves and a loosely panicled lateral inflorescence with orange-red flowers.

As with so many of these newly introduced species it takes some time to adapt itself to our conditions and whilst we have had it for some considerable time it is still not very happy and has made little growth. The loosely panicled lateral inflorescences bear orange-yellow blooms.

Echeveria turgida Rose

The name signifies "full, inflated". It has stemless, dense rosettes with obtuse, acuminate leaves, turgid, grey-green and only slightly pruinose. They are margined in red. The flower scape is 10cm. high, a one-sided raceme with pale vermillion flowers.

Plants distributed under this name by some nurseries have proved to be *E. derenbergii*.

Locality: It is found on limestone rock near Viesca, State of Coahuila, Mexico.

Propagation: From leaf cuttings taken in the spring.

Echeveria trianthina Rose

This species is native to the State of Hidalgo, Mexico. It is a small plant, offsetting freely and forming short stems. The leaves form a rosette and are oblanceolate with a concave upper surface and rounded below. Young leaves are intense red, ending in a tip but older leaves are greenish without the tips. The inflorescence is a one-sided raceme, with numerous reddish flowers.

We have found this to be one of the less easy species to grow.

Echeveria utcubambensis   Hutchinson ined.

As far as we know this name has yet to be validly published. We received it from Berkeley Botanic Gardens, California. It has small, pointed, glaucous leaves with a touch of pink about the colour. The stem elongates with age, with leaves scattered along its length in the manner of *Graptopetalum paraguayense* and similarly hangs over the side of the pot. New branches are formed from the base.

So far it has not flowered for us and we have no description of the inflorescence.

Echeveria vanvlietii   van Keppel

This new species from near Sucre in Bolivia has a short stem terminating in a dense rosette of spreading leaves. These are fleshy and oblong-oblanceolate, four times as long as wide. The upper surface is concave, the lower convex. The colour is rich green, pale grey-green under some conditions, flushed with purplish bronze.

The inflorescence is a single raceme with owl shaped green bracts. The nodding flowers are unique in the genus in being creamy-white.

Locality: They grow on steep slopes in excess of 6,000ft., where night frosts may occur.

Echeveria violescens   Walther

Sometimes met with as *E. gibbiflora metallica* in place of the true plant, which it closely resembles. It grows up to 60cm. high branching with age. The leaves are rounded at the apex and narrowed into a petiole at the base. The blade has the edges folded upwards, often undulate. They are glaucous green tinged reddish lilac.

The 60cm. inflorescence is often branched into several panicles with geranium pink flowers.

Locality: The Mexican habitat is not known.

Propagation: The rosette should be cut down from time to time and treated as a cutting, the remaining stump if left will throw out side shoots which can be pulled off and used as cuttings as soon as large enough.

Echeveria waltheri   Moran/Meyran

As this recent introduction was named after Eric Walther, who was an eminent specialist in the genus, one would have expected it to be something special. Instead it is one of the ugliest plants that ever graced a succulent collection. Except to complete a specialist collection of the genus it is not worth house room.

It consists of a single tall stem crowned by a very small rosette of about half a dozen leaves, resembling a miniature rosette of *E. coccinea.* We have tried to make it branch by beheading it but it only produces a single new shoot which continues to elongate as before.

The description mentions a red-stemmed inflorescence with white flowers tinged with pink, but these only succeed in looking washed out.

If it is desired to propagate it, this can easily be done by beheading and removing the new shoots as they are formed. These root readily as cuttings.

Echeveria whitei   Rose

Plants collected by Rausch and van Vliet in Bolivia in 1968 have been identified by van Keppel as Rose's *E. whitei.* They differ from *E. chilonensis* in their fine red flowers and other details and before Walther's decision that the two species are synonymous is accepted, more information is desirable.

There is great variability in collected Bolivian material in form, colour and size of both flowers and leaves so that the position of species is, at the moment, fluid.

The following plants have been offered by English nurseries in recent years although no trace of the names can be found in the literature. There is nothing to show whether they are species or hybrids, but they are probably the latter.

Echeveria mexecensis   Hort.

This is a most attractive, small growing variety, closest perhaps to *E. peacockii*

It is stemless, with a close rosette of many spatulate leaves each with a pronounced mucro. They are pale blue tinged with mauve edges and mucros and with a whitish bloom.

Inflorescence is a single cincinni, flowers pale pink, tapering to the tip, interior orange yellow hardly open, 18mm. long, usually 9 in number.

Echeveria purpurea   Hort.

This plant has no connection with either *E. atropurpurea* or *E. purpusorum*.

It has the habit of *E. gibbiflora* of which it may be hybrid. The leaves are obovate, with a small mucro, tapering and thickening towards the stem. The upper surface is concave with a well defined channel along the centre. The lower surface is convex and keeled. The colour is pale purple overlaid by an easily destroyed bloom.

Echeveria weingartiana   Hort.

This variety has a short thick stem surmounted by a loose rosette. The very thick leaves are boat shaped, very concave on the upper surface. They are light green, almost yellowy-green as they age but with reddish mottlings when young.

The thick inflorescence stem is pale yellowish red with bracts similar to the rosette leaves but smaller. The flowers are carried in a spike.

ECHEVERIA HYBRIDS

Among the hybrids can be found some of the best Echeveria for colour and leaf form but at the same time, many old hybrids are no improvement on original species and many could well be forgotten. The species will hybridise freely with each other so that cross fertilisation should be carried out selectively and not in many cases indiscriminately. It will be found that some variation in the same batch of seedlings usually result from cross pollination and only the best forms should be selected for naming and the clones propagated vegetatively either by leaf cuttings or offsets, the remaining seedlings being destroyed.

Generally, hybrids will be found easier in cultivation due to a natural vigour and are able to counter disease and winter problems associated with prolonged periods of cold and damp. This does not mean that winter care in watering and maintaining a reasonable minimum temperature can be overlooked, as the combination of damp and cold will cause rotting of the lower leaves and possibly complete disintegration of the rosette if a properly heated house is not available.

Where possible the originator and parentage details are included in the descriptions, but with many of the older and new hybrids these details are not known to the authors.

Echeveria x 'Blue Spur'   Hort.
Parentage: Not known
Originated: H. M. Butterfield

Originated about 1955 this plant was selected from the same batch of seedlings as the *gibbiflora* cultivar "Edna Spencer" and a distribution of it was made by the I.S.I. in 1962 No. I.S.I. 171.

This plant is interesting for its curious twisted leaf growth; they are green with a blue pruinose overlay, margins finely edged with red, leaves often slightly carunculated and producing long spur- or tooth-shaped growths from the base indicating some form of mutation. There is no formal-shaped rosette as it is continually branching or offsetting until a compact dome is formed. Details of flowers are not known to us.

Propagation: By removing the prolific offsets and treating as cuttings.

Echeveria x 'Cameo'   Brown Jr
    E. gibbiflora cv. Carunculata x E. x Edna Spencer

Originated by Mr. D. Wright of California 1961. Sister seedling to the hybrid *E. x* Paul Bunyan.

This highly embossed plant seems to have about reached the ultimate in carunculation and is a very interesting plant for its more compact and short stem growth.

The stem is about 15cm. high, 3cm. in diameter topped by a dense rosette of up to 30 leaves, the rosette is about 30cm. in diameter. The young leaves are pale green gradually lengthening until they are broadly spatulate, thickened at the base 15cm. long broadening to 7cm. wide, terminating in a pronounced tip. Older leaves becoming recurved and retuse, the colour gradually changing to pale blue with a tinge of pink. Lack of water during spring and summer will cause withering of the leaf tips.

Propagation: As for *E. gibbiflora v. Carunculata.*

Echeveria x 'Corymbosa'   Gosset
    E. agavoides x E. derenbergii

This plant resembles *E. agavoides* in habit and the inflorescence is typical of its other parent. The very thick, short, pointed leaves clothe the short stem thickly to the base. They are shining bright green entirely lacking in bloom. Older leaves have a red tip, the colour extending on the under surface as the leaves age. The flowers stand upright when open and are a rich orange-yellow in colour.

Propagation: By leaf cuttings taken in spring.

Echeveria x dasyphylla   Deleuil
      Parentage: *E. amoena x E. agavoides*

The stem is short with a dense rosette of cuneiform, imbricated obtuse leaves. These are brilliant green, tipped red. This must not be confused with *E. x dasyphylla* Hort., a branching plant, hybrid between *E. setosa* and *E. derenbergii*, the reverse cross of *E. x derosa* and very similar to it.

Echeveria x derosa   Hort.
      Parentage: *E. derenbergii x E. setosa*
      Originated: Von Roeder

This cross is a popular one and several clones have been named. It forms a domed rosette with a large number of leaves, practically stemless and up to 15cm. in diameter. The leaves are three times as long as wide, soft green with a red tip, glaucous but with a finely papillose margin. The numerous inflorescences are arched, with a few large flowers in spring. These have an orange red exterior but a yellow interior. "Worfield Wonder" is the most popular clone in England. On the continent its place is taken by "Hertzblut".
Propagation: By leaf cuttings.

Echeveria x derosa variegata   Hort.

Discovered by one of the authors in the Dutch commercial nursery of Mr. F. Hoogvliet in March 1972, selected from several thousand *E. x derosa* on display. Partial variegated forms have been noted before, but this clone is a particularly fine example, having at least half the leaf a linearly clear yellow, the remainder of the leaf is a soft green as the type, complete with red tip.

Echeveria x 'Doris Taylor'   Poindexter
      E. pulvinata x E. setosa

Originated by Dr. William Fuller Taylor, Head of the department of Biology, University High School, Berkeley, U.S.A. in 1932.

Type A.C.S. No. 3–420–522.

This popular plant forms a dark red trunk a few cm. high terminating in a many leaved, loose rosette 15–20cm. in diameter. The leaves are elongated, spatulate, terminating in a blunt point 9cm. long, 3cm. wide. They are pale green in colour, covered densely with short white hairs 2mm. long which may be reddish at the tips and for a short distance along the edges. The flower scapes usually two in number are up to 50cm. long and branching at the top. The fairly large flowers are orange-red. ◂

Propagation: By removal of offsets which are freely produced with age or by leaf cuttings.

Echeveria x fallax   Gosset
          Parentage: *E. derenbergii x E. elegans*

This is an interesting hybrid, valuable for its free flowering from April–May. It forms a tight rosette, 10cm. in diameter of 40 or more leaves. The leaves are pale blue, pruinose, the colour of *E. elegans*, 4cm. long, 4cm. broad, rounded with a well-developed mucro, the margin has a broad translucent opalescent border.

The flowers, usually seven in number, are carried on several cincinni giving continuous flowering over a long period, and are a delicate pale pink, with a yellow interior, 1cm. long, 1cm. wide when open, the calyx bracts tipped red. These are also sometimes spotted with red on the reverse.

Echeveria gilva x Walther   "Gilva" van Keppel
          Type: California Ac. Science No. 223895
     Parentage: *E. agavoides x E. elegans*   van Keppel

When Walther described this plant in 1935, he stated that

although only known from cultivated plants he considered it was not a hybrid, but a true species on the basis that the plant showed clearly the distinguishing characteristics of the series "Urbiniae" without the admixture of any foreign features. van Keppel, on the other hand, after conducting a series of experimental crosses in 1965–71 produced identical plants by crossing *E. agavoides x E. elegans* to an F3 generation. This leading cultivar is well known and popular in collections, although sometimes incorrectly sold commercially as *E. simulans*.

It has dense rosettes, 15cm. in diameter, older plants with many offsets. The leaves numerous, thick and fleshy with translucent leaf margins, colour apple green. The leaves often suffused reddish on both sides during February and March. Inflorescence a single cincinnus with pinkish red, yellow tipped flowers in spring.

Propagation: By leaf cuttings and removal of the many offsets from older plants which are then treated as normal cuttings.

Echeveria x gilva cv. 'Blue Surprise'   van Keppel

This blue cultivar which is derived as a somatic mutant of the cultivar "Gilva" should prove popular in collections once it is more freely available. It was discovered by van Keppel in a Dutch commercial nursery in 1954. It has the same vigorous growth and form of "Gilva".

Propagation: From leaf cuttings which we find do not revert to the green form.

Echeveria x graessneri cv. 'Eric Walther'   van Keppel
Parentage: *E. derenbergii x E. pulvinata*
Syn. Ex *haageana* ex Walth. nom. illeg.

Type plant van Keppel No. 5432 sent to the Herbarium of the I.O.S. Zurich. Named in honour of R. Graessner, Perleberg, Germany and E. Walther, California, U.S.A.

The plant forms a short 10–15cm. long stem, erect and branching from the base, offshoots lateral later ascending. The leaves are crowded into a dense rosette, covering each other unequally, flat above but somewhat upcurved, rounded beneath and indistinctly keeled, apex rounded, mucronate.

The leaf colour is glaucous green, edges and sometimes the upper part on the backside of the leaf reddish, surface granular-roughened by conspicuous epidermal cells, leaves are 6cm. long and 3cm. broad, thick and narrowing at the base to 1cm.

The inflorescence usually two in number are ascending to 12cm. long with salmon-orange flowers scarlet on the upper part and keel of segmentism later fading to yellow. The hybrid is valuable as it flowers three times a year, starting in January.

There are other clones from the same cross but, being very close to *E. derenbergii*, they have not been named. The plant has been distributed by continental growers as *E. x haageana*.

Propagation: From offsets and leaf cuttings taken in the spring.

Echeveria x haageana   Haage Jr amend van Keppel
           Parentage: *E. agavoides x E. derenbergii*

Parentage by previous authors:
   E. agavoides x E. derenbergii (Graessner)
   E. agavoides x E. pulchella (von Roeder, von Poellnitz)
   E agavoides x E. pulvinata (von Poellnitz)
   E. derenbergii x E. pulvinata (Walther)
   E. agavoides x E. elegans (van Keppel)

The former confused parentage of this plant was initially due to Haage Jr. omitting one of the parents from his original description in the catalogue issued in 1928. In his catalogue he offered this plant as a "novelty", in growth similar to *E. agavoides*, but much more rich flowering. Walther received a plant from Graessner in 1932 under the name of *E. x haageana* which he subsequently described in the American Journal in 1937. When we look at the hybrid of Walther's description we observe a quite different plant and to avoid further confusion van Keppel re-named this clone *E. x graessneri*. *E. haageana* is a stemless plant offsetting freely from the base. The leaves form a close rosette.

85

Echeveria haageana

They are oblong, acute, coming to a point, glaucous green in colour with translucent edges and a reddish mucro. The backs of the leaves are faintly keeled and flushed with red. The inflorescence is a cincinnus, the flowers bell-shaped, pinkish-red outside and yellow inside. Flowering period is in May–June.

Propagation: By removal of offsets or leaf cuttings.

Echeveria x 'Kircheriana'   Hort.
    Parentage: *E. derenbergii x E. Carnicolor* (Greassner)
        E. Carnicolor x derenbergii (von Poellnitz)
        E. derenbergii x E. pilosa (von Poellnitz)

The origin of this plant although in cultivation fairly common, is unknown, various experts on the genera have speculated on the correct parentage but investigations so far made by Van Keppel have proved Graessner was incorrect in stating the above parentage and why Von Poellnitz gave two possibilities as parentage we do not know because he never gave any explanation. Van Keppel is of the opinion that it is one of the clones belonging to the *E. x graessneri* complex.

In our experience it resembles a very vigorous growing *E. derenbergii* both in habitat and the inflorescence. With age it forms a stem up to 10cm. high.

Propagation: By leaf cuttings or offsets.

Echeveria x metallica   Hort.

The correct nomenclature of this plant although it is well known in England and on the Continent, is at present in some confusion, so it has been listed as it is distributed and sold by the Dutch trade. It should not be confused with *E. gibbiflora* var. *metallica*. Baker, which is quite a different plant or *E. acutifolia*: Lindley.

It quickly forms tall stems with a loose rosette of spatulate bronze green leaves which have a distinct channel, they are 20cm. long 10cm. wide. The flowering stem has short branches growing all round it in a sort of raceme with numerous coral rose flowers which do not open widely in late autumn.

This description fits to some extent the American plant called *E. flammea* Hort., of which the origin of is speculated on in Vol. xxvii, No. 6, of the *American Cactus Society Journal* in 1955, and except for the flame-like streaks which are said to develop in *E. flammea* in autumn they could well be the same plant, although these flame-like streaks could be caused through cultivation by planting out in the open for example.

Locality: Not known, although belonging to the gibbiflora complex it is considered by van Keppel to be a hybrid due to the flowers which appear to be sterile.

Propagation: By stem and leaf cuttings.

Echeveria x 'Hoveyi'   Rose
   Origin: Probably the collection of Hovey, Boston, U.S.A.

This plant was first described and pictured in *Horticulture* (Boston) 11:849, 1910 under Foreign Plant Introductions (without author). The same description is mentioned in the U.S. Dept. Bull. 223:39 1911 and is considered as the original description by Dr. Rose.

For many years *E. 'Hoveyi'* was thought to be a true species, although it is now clear that it is a plant of chimaerical origin and is a somatic mutant of *E. 'Zahnii'*. In European collections it grows no larger than 15–20cm. in diameter. The leaves are narrow, 5–10cm. long 2cm. broad at the widest part, they are variegated, pale green with broad white margins, tips uneven the white margins turning bright pink in early spring, leaves forming a loose spreading rosette on a short stem, branching with age. The flowering stem is a secund raceme bearing 6–12 pinkish flowers.

Propagation: By removal of offsets which are then treated as cuttings.

Echeveria x lancefolia   Deleuil
            Parentage: *E. rosea x E. glauca*

Described by Mons Deleuil in 1877 one year before Rollinson. It is dwarf and compact with a rosette of numerous lanceolate leaves, they are soft, glaucous blue suffused with pink.

Propagation: By offsets which when removed are treated as cuttings.

Echeveria x leucosina   Hort.
   Parentage: *E. leucotricha x E. potosina*
      Originated by G. C. Fuge

This hybrid slowly forms a stem, offsetting from the base, it is close to *E. leucotricha*. The lanceolate, pointed leaves are leaf green in colour, lacking the brown tip and puberulent instead of hairy, the leaves forming stiff upright loose rosettes. It appears to be a shy flowerer in cultivation as we have not seen the inflorescence although our plants have been in cultivation for some years.

Propagation: By removing offsets which should be treated as cuttings.

Echeveria x moovisii   Hort.

The parentage and originator is not known to us, but in appearance there is a resemblance to *E. multicaulis*. Leaves are in a loose rosette on the top of a short stem branching with age, and they are broadly obovate spatulate, ending in a short point, glossy, bright green but fringed with very short, fine hairs.

Echeveria x mutabilis   Deleuil
   E. linguaefolia x E. scheerii (Morren)
   E. linguaefolia x E. expatriata (Walther)
      Originated by Mons Deleuil about 1870

The true parentage of this hybrid is not confirmed but could well be as speculated by Walther as long ago as 1937. It is a good example of indiscriminate breeding and would be best forgotten, as it has few redeeming features.

It forms a tall 20–30cm. high stem topped with a lax rosette of 5–7cm. long, 2–3cm. broad, thick spatulate leaves, concave above, thick to the margins, colour a pale yellowish green. The inflorescence is laxly decumbent 25–75cm. long which terminates into a series of short branches carrying 2–5 pale green flowers. Flowering February–March.

Echeveria x 'Perle-von-Nurnberg'
Parentage: *E. gibbiflora metallica x E. potosina*
Originated by Graessner, Perleberg, Germany

One of the most popular and beautiful of the older hybrids. It forms a stem slowly and seldom offsets. The leaves, set in a close rosette, are shaped like *E. potosina* but are purplish in colour and strongly pruinose. The rosette may reach up to 15cm. in diameter. The flower scape is at first horizontal from the lower leaves and so closely set with leaf-like bracts as to look like an offset.

A variation in clones has led to many variental names being seen, for example "Pink Perle" and "Duchess of Nurnberg". From our observations there appears to be three clones in cultivation, Purple, Pink and Silver. The Pink variety never grows more than 8cm. in diameter, but as these colours can be produced by cultivation variation on the normal purple form, new cultivar names are considered superfluous.

Propagation: By leaf cuttings.

Echeveria x 'Pinky'   Hort.
Parentage: *E. shaviana x E. subrigida*

This is one of the more distinctive hybrids distributed by the I.S.I. number I.S.I. 697. It forms a close rosette of many leaves, stemless at least during its early years. Like *E. shaviana* it grows rapidly and a two-year-old plant can be 15cm. in diameter.

The lanceolate leaves are lightly covered with white farina tinged pink, the leaf margins bordered with pink.

Propogation: By leaf cuttings.

Echeveria x pulvi-carn   Walther
E. carnicolor x E. pulvinata
Originated by Victor Reiter Jr. 1933

This hybrid is near to *E. pulvinata* differing in its paler flowers, narrower leaves and shorter stem making for an altogether more compact plant. The influence of *E. carnicolor* appears to be only slight. It forms a short stem up to 4cm. high branching at the base. The narrower crowded leaves making a dense rosette, the leaves are 70mm. long, 25mm. broad and 8mm. thick, slightly upcurved shallowy concave above, rounded beneath coming to a point densely and finely covered in short hair. The colour is sap green but older leaves are tinged with red.

The inflorescence is a equilateral raceme 2 or more up to 60cm. tall with 25–30 flowers which are peach red outside, salmon-orange inside. Flowers in December and January.

Propagation: By removal of side shoots, or by leaf cuttings.

Echeveria x pulv-oliver   Walther
E. pulvinata x E. harmsii
Orginated by Victor Reiter Jr. 1932

This hybrid resembles *E. pulvinata* in habit, stem up to 10cm. high branching from the base. The leaves laxly arranged near the end of the branches are relatively thinner and more acute, erect to spreading shallowly concave above, rounded beneath 5cm. long by 2cm. broad, narrowed at the base to 5mm. wide. The colour is lime green, tipped with light red turning to walnut brown which extends to the margins. Inflorescences, usually 2 or more, are erect and 15–20cm. long, and carry 6 to 8 large coral red flowers.

From our experience it is shy to flower in this country unless given a rich compost and watered generously during summer.

Propagation: By removal of side shoots which are then treated as cuttings.

Echeveria x set-oliver   Walther
E. harmsii x E. setosa
Originated by Victor Reiter Jr. 1932

This hybrid is near *E. harmsii* in habit, being sub-shrubby, differing in the more numerous flowers borne on each scape, a slightly smaller corolla and relatively narrower, more crowded leaves with dense white hairs. The leaves are carried in loose rosettes, and are pubescent bright green in colour with maroon margins and tip, turning to mahogany brown in older leaves. They are about 6cm. long, 10–15mm. broad, 6–9mm. thick.

Stout flower scapes are formed from below the rosettes, erect, usually 2 or more and are simple bifid racemes up to 40cm. tall, brown in colour and carrying bracts as large as and similar to the leaves. Several flowers nearly as large as those of *E. harmsii* are carried, colour scarlet red, the edges and tip of each petal segment an apricot yellow. Flowers in November to January.

Propagation: By removal of side shoots which are then treated as cuttings, or by leaf cuttings.

Echeveria x rubella   von Poellnitz
            Parentage: *E. agavoides x E. cuspidata*

Catalogued by Haage and Schmidt in 1920. It forms a large rosette 15cm. in diameter. The leaves are broad, large and thick, wide at the base tapering to a point. They are shiny apple green without a trace of bloom, and grown in good light in winter the leaves become suffused red making the plant an attractive addition to any collection.

Echeveria x rubescens   Deleuil
            Parentage: *E. x imbricata x E. atropurpurea*

The leaves are large, broad and thick, wide at the base and tapering to a point, somewhat undulate. They are shining green suffused with deep reddish purple. The flowers, on a very long inflorescence, are a rich crimson.

Propagation: Is easy from leaf cuttings.

Echeveria x scaphylla   Deleuil
            Echeveria scaphopylla.   Berger
            Parentage: *E. agavoides x E. linguaefolia*

This is a very old, well-known hybrid described as long ago as

1872, and is often found in collections still under the incorrect name of scaphophylla as described by Berger in Gartenflora 53 : 205 fig. 27 in 1904.

It is a plant half way between its parents and this point can be seen quite distinctly. It slowly forms a stem of crowded thick turgid leaves, which are apple green and terminate in a sharp point, the tips brown on older leaves. The rosette is up to 10cm. in diameter.

Propagation: Is easy by leaf cuttings.

Echeveria x setorum c.v. 'Victor' van Keppel
Urbino-Echeveria angustata (van Laren)
Parentage: *E. setosa x E. purpusorem*
Originated by Victor Ploem of Kerkrade, Holland, 1922

This old hybrid was lost to general cultivation until van Keppel was able to re-introduce it in 1970, from plants propagated from stock originally belonging to Mr. Ploem.

It forms a single, regular shaped rosette, 10cm. in diameter offsetting with age. Leaves spatulate, ascending, concave above, keeled below, narrowed to the top and tapering into a very thin point. They are 4–8cm. long, 1.5cm. broad at the widest point tapering to the base, colour dark apple green, spotted red on the sides. The inflorescence, 2 or more 20cm. long is a single or bifid raceme with 10 or more red flowers tipped yellow. Flowering March–May.

Propagation: By removal of offsets or leaf cuttings taken in spring.

Echeveria x 'Vanbreen' van Keppel
E. derenbergii x E. carnicolor
Originated by J. A. van Breen, Nieuw Vennep, Holland, 1964
Type: van Keppel No. 6643, sent to the Herbarium of the I.O.S.
Zurich

In van Keppel's investigation in the origin of *E. x kircheriana* which was stated by Graessner about 1930 as a cross between *E. derenbergii* and *E. carnicolor* and by subsequent authors Von Poellnitz and Jacobsen, van Keppel received plants of the above which disproved the parentage of *E. x kircheriana* as being of this cross.

The resulting hybrid has a stemless dense 10–15cm. rosette of blue-green leaves in shape and size resembling *E. carnicolor* but is much more vigorous, scarcely glaucous and lacking the brown tips of the other parent. The inflorescence, carried sideways as in *E. carnicolor*, is well furnished with bracts but the orange flowers are smaller than *E. derenbergii*.

Propagation: This hybrid is easily increased by offsets and leaf cuttings.

Echeveria x 'Victor Reiter'   Hort.
Parentage: *E. agavoides* 'Prolifera' x *E. parrasensis*
Originated by F. Reinelt of Capitola, California

First distributed by the I.S.I. in 1970 reference No. I.S.I. 645. It forms large, stemless rosettes of stiff, thick pointed leaves. The leaves are brownish violet, with dark red tips, the inflorescence is tall, bifid, carrying a few red flowers. If given too much water or insufficient light the leaves turn dark green, vigorous growing the rosette quickly reaches up to 25cm. in diameter.

Propagation: From leaf cuttings taken in spring.

Echeveria x 'Zahnii'   van Keppel
E. Zahnii hort Cambridge
Parentage and originator unknown
Type: van Keppel No. 6437. Somatic reversion of *E. 'Hoveyi'* at Wassenaar, Holland 1964

There are no records of the origin of this plant but it is considered to be an Echeveria secunda with a larger species for example *E. rubromarginata* or *E. gigantea*. H. Hall U.S.A. in 1938 was the first to draw attention to reversion of *E. 'Hoveyi'* to a normal non-variegated plant.

Vegetatively this reversion was indentical with a plant known in England as *E. Zahnii* hort Cambridge. Because he had never seen flowers on either plant, he could not determine for certain their possible relationships.

The plants form a short stem topped by a loose rosette of spatulate leaves. These are fleshy, 7cm. long, 3.5cm. broad, margins white or reddish, sometimes wavy, and are channelled on the upper part, slightly incurved, back side convex slightly keeled, colour blue green, sometimes mottled with darker and lighter spots. The inflorescence part a cincinnus carrying 12–20 pinkish red flowers narrowly edged yellow, flowering July–August.

Propagation: By removal of offsets which are then treated as cuttings.

NEW AMERICAN HYBRIDS

The following list of American Hybrid Echeverias are fairly new to Britain and have not therefore been established in commercial or private collections long enough to describe with any accuracy.

The descriptions and mature sizes stated are known only from catalogues and our own observations of semi mature plants. One thing that can be stated is that the majority are vigorous, stout growing plants, some with outstanding features with regard to colour and form. They require a rich compost and an occasional summer feeding to ensure full development. This is best given by using one of the many proprietory liquid fertilisers at half strength, watering about every two weeks from June to the end of August, from the bottom.

E. x 'Ballerina'. Rosette 30cm. in diameter with crowded leaves, upper surface concave with a well defined channel, leaf margins wavy. Older leaves reflexed margins and tips flushed pink.

E. x 'Berkeley'. Originated by H. M. Butterfield. A slow stem-forming plant, topped by a rosette 25cm. in diameter of pale blue pruinose leaves, the young leaves are flushed pink with deeper pink margins. Leaves folded with a well defined channel and have wavy leaf margins.

E. x 'Bittersweet'. This is a stout, tall, vigorous hybrid seldom branching, similar in habit to *E. gibbiflora*, the stem is bare topped with a rosette of up to 20 broad spatulate leaves, which are narrow and fleshy at the base, the colour of light mahogany, the leaf margins crimped and undulating.

E. x 'Blondie'. Originated by D. Wright, California. This hybrid is noted for its pale lemon green colour. It slowly forms a stem topped by a rosette 18cm. in diameter of broad leaves with wavy leaf margins. It forms offsets from the base.

E. x 'Bouquet'. Originated by D. Wright, California. Known only from catalogue description. This appears to be a sub-shrub offsetting from the base. Stems bare, topped with a rosette of green crowded leaves. The plant being noted for its large, yellow and orange flowers.

E. x 'Harry Butterfield'. Originated by H. M. Butterfield. This forms a stem slowly topped by a large rosette 30cm. in diameter of blue-green leaves with a red beaded crinkly margin.

E. x 'Mary Butterfield'. Forming a single 20cm. rosette this hybrid has long reflexed leaves, which are folded with a well defined channel, the margins undulating. The colour is mauve with a tinge of pink, the leaves heavily pruinose.

E. x 'Candy Wright'. Originated by D. Wright, California. This is one of the more delicate hybrids and it forms a rosette 12cm. in diameter. The leaves are crowded and broadly spatulate tapering at the base, and are a deep pink with dark pink wavy margins.

E. x 'Chantilly'. Originated by D. Wright, California. The pale blue leaves are upturned, undulating flecked with red. Lightly pruinose, they form a loose 30cm. diameter rosette. The leaf margins are crimped and irregular.

E. x 'Cinderella'. Originated by D. Wright, California. This is a large growing, vigorous hybrid, and slowly forms a stem, off-setting from the base. The short stem is topped with a loose

30cm. rosette of broad spatulate upturned leaves. These are a deep purple or plum colour, pruinose, with dark red margins.

E. x 'Crinkles'. Originated by H. M. Butterfield. Known only from a catalogue description, this is one of the smaller of the new hybrids. It forms close rosettes of blue/green leaves, the margins wavy, edged pink.

E. x Crenulata 'Royal Curl'. Known only from catalogues without description.

E. x 'Curly Locks'. Originated by H. M. Butterfield. This hybrid is now wider known in England and popular among collectors. It forms a close rosette 15cm. in diameter of blue, slightly pruinose leaves. These are oblong spatulate, the edges folded up with very wavy margins, older leaves retuse. Offsets are produced freely from the base.

E. x 'De Candolle'. Known only from catalogues, description incomplete, but appears to form a loose rosette of undulating pale mauve leaves.

E. x 'Edna Spencer'. Originated by H. M. Butterfield. This plant has *E. gibbiflora var. carunculata* in its parentage, and it slowly forms a stem topped by a tight rosette of carunculated pale blue leaves, which are broadly spatulate with wavy margins. It is compact, the rosette growing no larger than 15cm. in diameter.

E. x 'Fleur D'or'. Originated by D. Wright, California. Usually stemless, it has a tight formal rosette of almost linear leaves 5cm. long, 1cm. wide, pointed and thick with red margins. They are hardly pruinose and apple green in colour. It forms a single flower spike, with yellow flowers. The offsets which are produced freely appear from between the leaves of mature plants.

E. x 'Flying Cloud'. Originated by D. Wright, California. This plant is noted for its unusual variegated leaves, which are broadly spatulate, upturned with pink margins. They are crenulate, irregular. The leaves flushed pink from the tip in early spring. It slowly forms a stem and occasionally offsets are produced from the base.

E. x 'Giant Mexican Firecracker'. Originated by Dr. Uhl, Cornell University. Noted for its large orange and red flowers, this is

G   97

a sub-shrub branching freely with age, the branches topped with loose rosettes of pale green leaves. These are spatulate terminating in a blunt point and covered with short white hairs which may be brownish at the tips and for a short distance along the edges.

E. x 'Gypsy'. Originated by D. Wright, California. Noted for its large shape and form, it slowly forms a stem which carries a number of broad spatulate leaves in a loose rosette 35cm. in diameter. The leaves are folded up with a well defined channel, the margins undulating with crinate edges. The colour is a rich dark pink.

E. x 'Harrietta'. This plant slowly forms a stem topped by a loose rosette of broadly tapering leaves, these are up to 15cm. long folded almost double, margins undulating. At first they are green with red margins but gradually change to a reddish purple with age.

E. x 'Katella II'. Originated by D. Wright, California. This is a vigorous growing plant and slowly forms a stem branching from the base. The leaves are green, undulating, broad and spatulate, covered in an overlay of pink bloom which deepens to red in bright sunlight, margins crenate, edged a deep pink. The loose rosette is large, up to 30cm. in diameter.

E. x 'Katella IV'. Originated by D. Wright, California. This is similar to the previous description, more compact, rosettes up to 20cm. in diameter. Leaves spatulate, upturned, undulating with curly margins. They are glaucous green edged with red.

E. x 'La Feme'. Originated by D. Wright, California. The leaves of this plant are coloured by an unusual clear skin pink. It quickly forms a bare stem topped by a 15cm. rosette of broad undulating leaves. The leaf margins are translucent and crenate.

E. x 'Lemonade'. Originated by D. Wright, California. Imperfectly known by the authors. It has variegated leaves and is stem forming. The rosettes reaching 15cm. in diameter.

E. x 'Lemon Twist'. Originated by J. Napton. Imperfectly known by the authors. This is a stem forming plant offsetting from the base. The stem is bare topped by a loose rosette of pale green leaves.

E. x 'Marvella'. Originated by D. Wright, California. Imperfectly known by the authors. This appears to be a vigorous growing plant which quickly forms a stem, topped by a loose rosette of dark pink undulating leaves. These are pruinose, the overlay red and green.

E. x 'Meridian'. Originated by D. Wright, California. This hybrid is well known in English collections for its vigorous growth and was one of the first of the new hybrids to be imported. It slowly forms a stout stem topped by a loose 20cm. rosette of slightly pruinose, broad, spatulate leaves, which are green undulating with red margins. It produces offsets occasionally from the base.

E. x 'Mary Diane'. New introduction and imperfectly known to describe.

E. x 'Mahogany Rose'. New introduction and imperfectly known to describe.

E. x 'Nubbles'. Originated by M. Kimnack, California. This is a stem-forming plant with a 20cm. rosette of loose carunculated leaves. Prior to this introduction all carunculated plants had pale blue or mauve leaves, this is an unusual orange-brown colour.

E. x 'Party Dress'. Originated by D. Wright, California. This is a vigorous growing hybrid, the leaves loosely arranged in a 30cm. rosette on a short stem. They are broad, spatulate, thick and fleshy at the base, undulating with crenulate margins edged red. The leaves are a glaucous blue tinged with pink, occasionally flecked with white on the reverse.

E. x 'Paul Bunyan'. Originated by D. Wright, California. Similar to *E. gibbiflora cv. carunculata* in habit, the leaves are loosely arranged in a 30cm. rosette. It differs from carunculata in its undulating leaf margins and larger pronounced gibbious protuberances on the leaves.

E. x 'Ruth Jane'. A new introduction without description. From our immature plants it would appear to be of medium size in growth, stem-forming with deep pink crenate edged undulating spatulate leaves, the leaf margins are a darker pink.

E. x 'Silveron Red'. Originated by D. Wright, California. This is one of the more distinct hybrids. It forms a stem slowly topped by a 25cm. rosette of up to 20 leaves, which are broadly spatulate, upturned with a distinct keel, the colour is dark red with an overlay of bloom making them appear silvery, the leaf margins are crenate and edged bright red.

E. x 'Sugard'. Originated by Dr. Uhl, Cornell University. This is a sub shrub branching with age, our plants too immature even to offer a description.

BIBLIOGRAPHY

Baker, J. G. *Saunders Refugium Botanicum*, 1869–1870.

Bailey, L. H. *Standard Cyclop. Hortic. 2*, 1922.

Berger. *Crassulaceae*, 1930.

Britton and Rose. *Bulletin New York Bot. Garden. 3*, 1903.

Britton and Rose. *North American Flora, 22 part 1*, 1905

Ginns, R. *Nat. Cactus & Succulent Society Handbook 1*, 1968.

Graff, A. B. *Exotica. 3*, 1965.

Jacobsen, H. *Handbook of Succulent Plants*, 1959 Vol. I and II.

Keppel, J. C. van. *Succulenta Journals*, 1960–1968.

Lindley, J. *Botanical Register*, 1829–1848.

Lemaire, C. *Illustr. Hort. 9*, 1862.

Moran, R. *Cactus and Succulent Journal of America*, 1961–1966.

Morren, E. *Belgique Horticole*, 1874–1875.

Poellnitz, K. von. *Fedde's Rep.*, 1936.

Walther, E. *Cactus and Succulent Journal of America*, 1935–1959.

APPENDIX A

Species not apparently in cultivation in England
The authors have not yet met with the following species and would be glad to hear from anyone in possession of them.

		Locality
E. *aequatoralis*	Rose	Equador
E. *ballsii*	Walther	Columbia, Dept. Boyaka
E. *bracteolata*	Klotzsch et Otto	Venezuala, nr. Caracas
E. *canaliculata*	Hook	Mexico; Hidalgo
E. *carminea*	Alexander	Mexico; Oaxaca
E. *chiapensis*	Rose	Mexico; Chiapas
E. *chiclensis* (Ball)	Bgr.	Peru; Oroya and Matucana
syn. E. *backbergii*	v. Poelln.	
syn. E. *neglecta*	v. Poelln.	
E. *crassicaulis*	Walther	Mexico; Federal Distr.
E. *cuencaensis*	v. Poelln.	Equador; nr. Cuenca
syn. E. *ingens*	Rose	
E. *elatior*	Walther	Mexico; Hidalgo
E. *eurychlamys* (Diels)	Brg.	Peru; Dept. Cajamarca
E. *globuliflora*	Walther	
E. *globulosa*	Moran	Mexico; Oaxaca
E. *goldiana*	Walther	
E. *juarenzensis*	Walther	Mexico; Oaxaca
E. *longissima*	Walther	Mexico; Puebla and Oaxaca
E. *longiflora*	Walther	Mexico; Guerrero
E. *lozanii*	Rose	Mexico; Jalisco
E. *meyreniana*	Walther	
E. *minima*	Meyran	
E. *montana*	Rose	Mexico; Oaxaca
E. *omiltemiana*	Matuda	
E. *pachanoi*	Rose	Equador; nr. Santa Rosa de Canar
E. *parrasensis*	Walther	Mexico; Coahuila
E. *penduliflora*	Walther	Mexico; Oaxaca
E. *peruviana*	Meyen	Peru, Argentina; Prov. Jujuy
syn. E. *buchtinii*	v. Poelln.	
E. *pinetorum*	Rose	Mexico; Chiapas
E. *platyphylla*	Rose	Mexico; Hidalgo
E. *procera*	Moran	
E. *rubromarginata*	Rose	Mexico; Vera Cruz
syn. E. *gloriosa*	Rose	
E. *scheerii*	Lindley	Mexico; Chihuahua
E. *sprucei*	Baker	Equador; Ambato

E. teretifolia	de Candolle	Mexico; Hidalgo
syn. *E. subulifolia*	Morren	
E. tolucensis	Rose	Mexico; State of Mexico
E. turgida	Rose	Mexico; Coahuila
E. valvata	Moran	
E. viridissima	Walther	Mexico; Oaxaca
E. walpoliana	Rose	Mexico; Luis Potosi

APPENDIX B

Readers may meet with plants labelled as Echeverias under the following names. Whilst there names were valid at one time all these plants have been transferred to Dudleya and should no longer be considered as Echeverias. Certain of them, such as angustiflora and californica, are met with as names for certain hybrid Echeverias as well as for Dudleyas whilst others, such as *purpusii*, are sufficiently close to the names of true Echeverias i.e. *E. purpusorum*, for mistakes to occur.

DUDLEYAS

abramsii	cymosa	orcuttii
acuminata	delicata	ovatifolia
albida	densiflora	palensis
albiflora	diabolic	palmeri
aloides	eastwoodiae	parishii
amadorana	edulis	parva
angustiflora	elongata	pauciflora
anthonyi	farinosa	plattiana
argentea	greenei	pulverulenta
arizonica	hallii	purpusii
attentuata	hassei	reflexa
bernadina	helleri	rigida
brandegei	ingens	rigidiflora
brauntonii	insularis	robusta
brevipes	jepsonii	rubens
bryceae	lagunensis	saxosa
caespitosa	lanceolata	semiteres
californica	laxa	septentrionalis
candelabrum	linearis	setchelli
candida	lingular	tennis
collomiae	minor	traskiae
compacta	monicae	virens
congesta	nevadensis	viscida
cotyledon	nubigena	xantii
cultrata	nudicaulis	

A list of authenticated Echeveria which are nearly all derived from field collected material, distributed by the International Succulent Institute since 1958. These plants were only offered once and are unrepeatable.

I.S.I.

176	*E. crassicaulis*	Walther	List 1	1958
177	*E. chiapensis*	Von Poelln.	List 1	1958
178	*E. pumila*	Baker	List 1	1958
182	*E. subrigida* (Robins & Seat)	Rose	List 1	1958
168	*E. halbingeri*	Walther	List 2	1959
268	*E. viridissima*	Walther	List 2	1959
269	*E. affinis*	Walther	List 2	1959
155	*E. potosina*	Walther	List 3	1959
298	*E. turgida*	Rose	List 3	1959
321	*E. agavoides var. Nov*		List 4	1960
322	*E. agavoides var. 'Corderoyi'*	Von Poelln.	List 4	1960
331	*E. craigiana*	Walther	List 4	1960
338	*E. simulans*	Rose	List 4	1960
372	*E. spectabilis*	Alex	List 5	1960
196	*E. hetrosepala*	Rose	List 6	1961
197	*E. semivestita var. floresiana*	Walther	List 6	1961
198	*E. trianthina*	Rose	List 6	1961
215	*E. gigantea*	Rose and Purpus	List 7	1961
164	*E. bella*	Alex	List 8	1962
171	*E. 'Blue Spur'*		List 8	1962
172	*E. sp. (acutifolia)?*		List 8	1962
418	*E. alpina*	Walther		1963
419	*E. ciliata*	Moran		1963
420	*E. nodulosa* (Baker)	Otto		1963
421	*E. pulidonis*	Walther		1963

No list issued in 1964

454	*E. x 'Ballerina'*	Hort.	1965
455	*E. Sanchez-mejoradai*	Walther	1965
456	*E. shaviana*	Walther	1965
492	*E. chihuahuaensis*	Von Poelln.	1966
493	*E. dactylifera*	Walther	1966
494	*E. gibbiflora v carunculata*		1966
495	*E. harmsii (Rose)*	Macbride	1966
496	*E. lindsayana*	Walther	1966
497	*E. macdougallii*	Walther	1966
521	*E. purpursorum*	Berger	1967
523	*E. waltherii*	Moran and Meyran	1967
542	*E. moranii*	Walther	1968

1969   No Echeverias offered

I.S.I.

642	*E. chihuahuaensis var 'Ruby Blush'*		1970
643	*E. obtusifolia*	Rose	1970
644	*E. sessilifolia*	Rose	1970
645	*E. x 'Victor Reiter'*		1970
697	*E. x 'Pinky'*		1971
756	*E. gibbiflora*	D.C.	1972

SUPPLIERS OF ECHEVERIAS

The following nurseries are suppliers or growers of Echeverias. The authors have listed them in alphabetical order only for the convenience of readers and it should not be assumed that any nursery omitted from the list is unreliable or in any way inferior.

AMERICAN NURSERIES

Grigsby Cactus Gardens,
2354, Bella Vista Drive,
Vista, California 92083. U.S.A.

International Succulent Institute, (I.S.I.)
Secretary, J. W. Dodson,
10, Corte Sombritea,
Orinda, California 94563. U.S.A.

Wright, D.
11011, Tarawa Drive,
Los Alamitos, California 90720. U.S.A.

ENGLISH NURSERIES

Carruthers, L.
Cadley Miniature Plants,
13, St. Catherines Drive,
Fulwood, Preston, Lancs. PR2 3RL.
Agents for D. Wright, California Hybrids.

Innes, C. F.
Holly Gate Nurseries Ltd.,
Billingshurst Lane,
Ashington, Sussex.

International Succulent Institute, (I.S.I.)
British Agent: N. E. Wilbraham,
"Nan-Gwarra", 7, Marlborough Drive, Tytherington,
Macclesfield, Cheshire.

INDEX

*of specific names in alphabetical order
principle references in boldface type*

107